20 - SFB

13061733

INTERNATIONAL SERIES OF MONOGRAPHS ON
ANALYTICAL CHEMISTRY
GENERAL EDITORS: R. BELCHER and L. GORDON

Volume 1

MICROANALYSIS
BY THE RING OVEN TECHNIQUE

OTHER TITLES IN THE SERIES ON ANALYTICAL CHEMISTRY

Vol. 2. CROUTHAMEL (Ed.) — Applied Gamma-Ray Spectrometry
Vol. 3. VICKERY — The Analytical Chemistry of the Rare Earths

MICROANALYSIS
BY THE
RING OVEN TECHNIQUE

By

HERBERT WEISZ
Technische Hochschule, Vienna

PERGAMON PRESS
NEW YORK · OXFORD · LONDON · PARIS
1961

PERGAMON PRESS INC.
122 E. 55th Street, New York 22, N. Y.
P. O. Box 47715, Los Angeles, California

PERGAMON PRESS LTD.
Headington Hill Hall, Oxford
4 & 5 Fitzroy Square, London W. 1.

PERGAMON PRESS S.A.R.L.
24 Rue des Écoles, Paris Vᵉ

PERGAMON PRESS G.m.b.H.
Kaiserstrasse 75, Frankfurt am Main

CONTENTS

	Page
Foreword	7
Preface	9
Introduction	11
I. THE APPARATUS AND ITS USE	15
A. *The ring oven*	15
B. *The gas generator*	20
C. *The sample pipette and glass holder*	22
II. QUALITATIVE ANALYSIS	25
A. *Without separations*	25
B. *Separations*	26
(1) Into two groups	26
(2) Into three groups	27
(3) Separation of substances already collected in a particular group	28
C. *Systematic schemes for the analysis of metal ions*	32
(1) Separation scheme for 14 metal ions	34
(2) Separation scheme using "washing out and washing in" techniques	44
(3) Separation scheme using liquid-liquid extraction methods	45
D. *Reactions for metal ions*	47
E. *Reactions for acid radicals*	56
F. *Practical applications*	62
(1) Identification of fluoride ion	62

(2) Separation of molybdenum and tungsten   64
(3) Separation of uranium from thorium, bismuth and lead   65
(4) Some other applications   66

G. *Reagents and filter paper*   67

III. SEMI-QUANTITATIVE ANALYSIS   69

A. *Spot colorimetry*   69

B. *Spot colorimetry with the ring oven method*   70

(1) Determination of iron   72
(2) Determination of other metals   76
(3) Removal of interfering ions   79

C. *The universal standard scale*   80

IV. THE RING OVEN METHOD COMBINED WITH OTHER TECHNIQUES   87

A. *Ring oven method and electrography*   87

(1) Qualitative analysis   88
(2) Semi-quantitative analysis   89
(3) Sorting of steels   91

B. *Radiochemical applications*   92

C. *The ring oven as extractor*   94

D. *The ring oven and paper chromatography*   95

CONCLUSION   101

LIST OF RING OVEN PUBLICATIONS   103

REFERENCES   105

Subject Index   109

FOREWORD

WHEN I visited the famous Institute for Analytical Chemistry at the Technische Hochschule in Vienna for the first time after World War II, I learned of the original approaches of Dr. Herbert Weisz to the problems of spot test analysis and the chemistry of specific, selective and sensitive reactions.

During my next visit, Dr. Weisz demonstrated to me his first simple model of the ring oven. I recognized immediately that the ring oven technique would fill an important gap in the exploration of spot tests.

During the subsequent years, Dr. Weisz indefatigably pursued a programme of research with the ring oven and published many interesting papers on the subject. The ring oven method which Dr. Weisz created is now recognized all over the world and is used in many fields of analytical chemistry. The potential uses of this method in qualitative and semi-quantitative analysis, radiochemistry, paper chromatography etc. are most promising.

The present state of the ring oven technique demanded the preparation of a monograph on this subject. It is therefore with much personal pleasure that I recommend this first monograph on the ring oven which in my opinion represents an important milestone in spot test analysis.

Rio de Janeiro, June 1959.

PREFACE

THE ever-growing importance of microtechniques in analytical chemistry will, I hope, justify the writing of this monograph. There was a need for a method capable of handling extremely small samples which eight years ago stimulated me to develop the ring oven method. Since then it has been applied and extended by many other chemists. I have been fortunate to be encouraged to continue my work by many colleagues. Therefore my gratitude is due in the first instance to Prof. R. Strebinger, Vienna, Prof. F. Feigl, Rio de Janeiro, and Prof. R. Belcher, Birmingham, the latter who also suggested that I write this monograph.

The editors of this series, Prof. R. Belcher and Prof. L. Gordon, Cleveland, are to be thanked for a number of suggestions which improved the lay-out of the manuscript.

HERBERT WEISZ

Vienna, September 1959.

INTRODUCTION

In qualitative or quantitative analysis, separation of the substances contained in the sample into one or more groups is one of the most important steps. The separation steps must be selected in such a way, that the substances which are collected together in one group do not interfere with the subsequent identification or determination of each substance in the group.

Apart from special techniques, such as distillation or paper chromatography, the methods of analytical separation depend on the conversion of one, or more, parts of the mixture into insoluble compounds which are separated by filtration. This demands a number of chemical operations. The component to be separated must be precipitated by means of a suitable reagent; the precipitate must be filtered and washed; the separated precipitate must be redissolved ; and very often it is necessary to concentrate the filtrate as well as the redissolved precipitate.

Lack of sufficient test material is frequently a disadvantage especially when many substances have to be detected or determined. It may not always be practicable to dilute the test solution in order to obtain a more easily handled volume, because substances which are present in low concentrations may be diluted to a point where it becomes impossible to identify them.

If only a volume of 1 microlitre (μl) were available, it would be virtually impossible to achieve a separation by one of the usual methods of filtration or centrifugation. It would, however, be possible to place the drop on filter paper and to add some reagent which would localize one or more components of the mixture as a precipitate on the paper.

The soluble portions, that is, those which are not affected by the reagent, could then be eluted to the outer zone of the paper by means of the capillarity of the filter paper. The procedure can be illustrated by the following example.

A drop of solution contains copper(II) and iron(III) which are to be identified with potassium ferrocyanide. Separation is essential because both ions react with the reagent ; either the copper can be fixed with hydrogen sulphide in acidic solution or the iron can be precipitated with ammonium hydroxide. Thus, one of the two metals is fixed on the paper and the unprecipitated component can be washed into the outer zone with a suitable solvent — hydrochloric acid or ammonium hydroxide depending on which precipitant has been used.

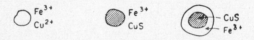

At this stage, difficulties begin to arise ; for when only a little solvent is used in the washing process, the separation cannot be complete. But when the washing is done thoroughly until, for example, the iron is completely removed from the copper sulphide spot, a large area of irregular shape, in which the iron is very much diluted, is obtained. Despite such difficulties, this method of separation has been widely and successfully used in spot analysis. For example, in the separation of barium and strontium on potassium dichromate paper,[1] strontium chromate is more soluble than the barium salt and therefore migrates into the outer zone of the spot where it can be identified with sodium rhodizonate solution.

However, for this technique to be generally applicable the above difficulties had to be overcome. A method had to be developed by which the unprecipitated portions could be completely removed from a precipitate fixed on filter paper without enlargement of the area of the "secondary" spot and without any decrease in the concentration of the washed-out substances.

This could be achieved by collecting the dissolved components in a previously determined place, where they could again be concentrated. Several simple forms of apparatus have been developed for this purpose and these will be described in the first chapter.

This "Ring Oven Technique" was originally developed as a qualitative separation technique for extremely minute samples, but it has found wide application in different branches of analytical chemistry. Within the past few years, it has been extended to semi-quantitative analysis, to the analysis of radioactive substances, to electrographic analysis, and the like. In the following chapters, the various applications of the ring oven technique are surveyed.

Chapter I

THE APPARATUS AND ITS USE

A. The Ring Oven

The ring oven *(Ringofen, four annulaire, estufa anular, fornello in forma di annello)*[2] serves the purpose of controlling the washing out of the unprecipitated components from a precipitate fixed on filter paper and of concentrating them again in a previously determined position.

Figure 1 illustrates the ring oven. A cylindrical block of aluminium, 35 mm high and of 55 mm diameter, carries a central bore-hole of 22 mm diameter (dotted lines). A heating wire is installed in this block which is insulated with asbestos. The heating block, *H*, is placed in the base plate, *U*, which also has a 22 mm bore-hole corresponding to that in the heating block. The body is supported on a tripod, *F*.

Gl is a small glass tube, 60 mm long, which is adjustable in height and

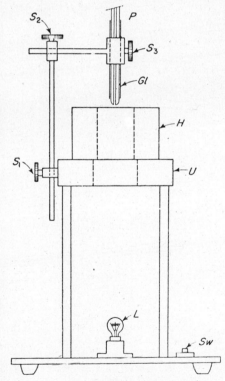

Fig. 1. The ring oven

position by means of three screws, S_1, S_2, and S_3. It serves as a guide tube for the capillary pipette, P, which just fits into it. The guide tube must stand vertically and must point exactly to the middle of the bore-hole, ending a few millimeters above the surface of the block. The pipette and the guide tube are centred by allowing the pipette to drop gently on to a small brass block with a central hole which just fits into the bore-hole of the ring oven, as shown in Fig. 2. A small electric lamp, L, below the heating block allows the edge of the oven to be seen and so enables the elution to be controlled more precisely. Sw is a push-button switch for the electric lamp. The heating wire uses about 20 W at 28 V; an adjustable resistance, or, better, a variable transformer (Variac) can be used to regulate the temperature of the heating block. The surface temperature must be about 105 to 110°C when aqueous solutions are used ; in general, it should be a few degrees above the boiling point of the solvent used for washing out. The temperature of the oven remains reasonably constant once the apparatus has been set. A different temperature may be required when organic solvents are used (see the chapter on "Extractions").

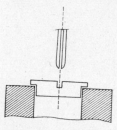

FIG. 2. Centering of the washing-pipette

A type of ring oven which is commercially available is shown in Fig. 3.

The ring oven which is described above is made of aluminium but various other materials can also be used, e. g. copper, stainless steel, gilded copper, etc. For very delicate analyses, plates of platinum or gold can be mounted on the surface of the heating block.

A glass ring oven (Fig. 4) has been described by Ballczo.[3] In this, the hollow glass body, G, which has the same dimensions as the usual metal ring oven, is connected with a condenser on one side and with a 100-ml glass flask on the other side. The flask contains 50 ml of a suitable bath-liquid which has a boiling point about 10°C above the surface temperature desired on the ring oven. When aqueous solutions

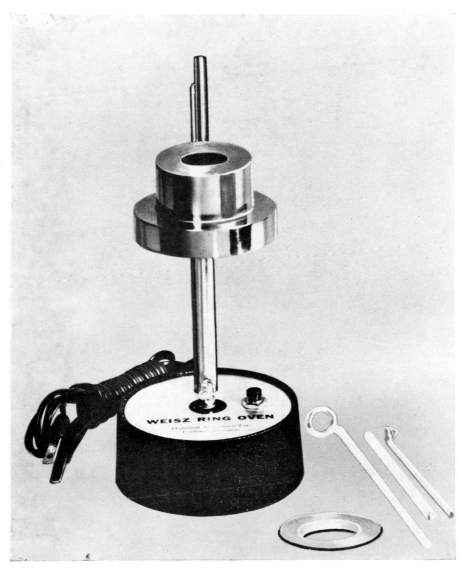

Fig. 3. Commercially available ring oven (courtesy National Appliance Company, Portland, Oregon, U.S.A.)

are used, a surface temperature of 105 to 110°C is necessary; sym-tetrachloroethylene (b.p. 121°C) is suitable. The bath liquid can be heated with a conventional gas or electric heater.

The Plexiglas ring, P, is fixed to the glass body, G, by means of three metal screws, S. The inner diameter of this ring is exactly the same as that of the filter papers used, 55 mm, so that the paper can always be placed exactly in the same position with the spot centred. Although this is not always necessary, it is advantageous in many cases. The Plexiglas ring also carries the metal holder with the centred glass guide tube for the capillary pipette.

The following example serves to show the mode of operation of the ring oven.

A drop of iron(III) chloride solution (1:10,000 dilution) is placed in the centre of a round filter paper. Only quantitative grade filter paper can be used ; Schleicher-Schüll 589² and Whatman No. 40 papers have been used for most ring oven work. The filter paper is placed on the hot ring oven so that the spot of solution lies centrally just under-

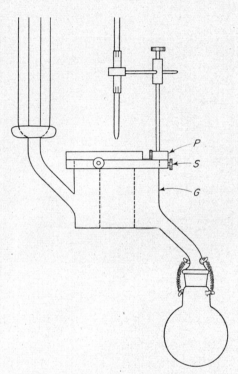

Fig. 4. The glass ring oven

neath the guide tube. The filter paper is kept in place by means of a porcelain or glass ring which has an inner diameter of about 25 mm.

All the iron chloride is then washed out with $0.05N$ hydro-chloric acid by means of a capillary pipette. This pipette is filled simply by touching it to the surface of the solvent, and is then placed upon the iron chloride spot through the guiding glass tube. The filter paper absorbs the solvent (in this case, the 0.05N hydrochloric acid) and the iron chloride migrates. The wet spot spreads concentrically and the pipette is refilled and again placed on the spot.

When the liquid reaches the edge of the bore-hole of the hot heating block, the solvent vaporizes, hence the size of the wet spot can never exceed the diameter of the bore-hole (22 mm).

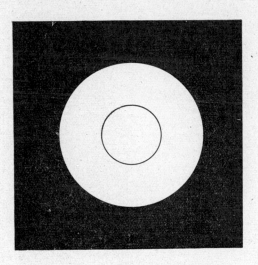

The dissolved components are transported to this point where they remain as a sharply defined ring zone. After the washing has been repeated 10 times, the iron chloride is completely concentrated in this ring zone. The flow of solvent from the pipette need not be regulated because the volume of the pipette is very small (the inner diameter of the capillary is about 0.1 mm) and because only as much liquid can leave the pipette as the paper can absorb.

Fig. 5. 0.15 μg iron

The entire procedure takes only one or two minutes.

The filter paper can then be dried in a drying oven, by means of an infrared lamp, or, preferably, with a hot air drier. It is then sprayed with, or dipped in, a 1% aqueous solution of potassium ferrocyanide whereupon the well-known Prussian blue colour appears in the ring zone; a well-defined, blue ring of 22 mm diameter appears where all the iron has been concentrated on the filter paper.

Because the inner part of the circle is completely free of iron, it is uncoloured. Fig. 5 shows such an iron ring obtained with 1.05 μg of iron.

The actual area of the ring, which is as thin as a pencil line, is quite small. Even if the width of the ring were 1 mm, the area of the ring would be less than 70 mm², i. e.,

$$2\pi r \times \text{width} = 22 \times 3.14 \times 1 = 69.1 \text{ mm}^2$$

The ring is therefore smaller than a spot of 10 mm diameter which corresponds to a drop volume of about 1.5 μl, i. e.,

$$\pi r^2 = 25 \times 3.14 = 78.50 \text{ mm}^2$$

However, with the concentrations normally used in microchemical work the ring zone is generally narrower, i. e. 0.1—0.3 mm, so that the area of the ring zone is even smaller, or about 7—20 mm². Thus *the actual concentrations of the eluted substances in the ring zone are three to ten times greater than in the original spot.*

The width of the rings can be measured under the microscope with an ocular micrometer or, better, by epidiascopic projection of the rings ; the width of the projected rings can be readily measured and compared with the known diameter of the ring (22 mm).

The process of elution on the ring oven can be readily demonstrated when a drop of solution containing a fluorescent compound, such as quinine sulphate, is placed on the paper and washed out with distilled water ; the progress of the extraction procedure can be seen under ultraviolet light.

If several ions migrate with the solvent and have to be detected in the ring zone, the dry filter paper is cut into as many sectors as required for the individual identification reactions. The ring has a circumference of about 70 mm, hence it can be divided into at least 10 sectors. When any sector is treated with a suitable reagent, the circular arc of length 7 mm develops the same colour intensity as the whole ring would have done, and the tests can be used with the same confidence.

When identification reactions are used, care must be taken that the sharply defined ring zone containing the precipitates does not become blurred.

2*

In regard to the sensitivity of spot reactions carried out in this way, experience has shown that if the concentration of an ion in the test drop is sufficient for a normal spot reaction, then the ion can also be identified in an aliquot part of the ring zone. In essence, the practical identification limit in ring oven tests is improved by at least ten times.

B. The Gas Generator

When separations are required, some part of the material must be fixed on the sample spot on the filter paper by suitable precipitation procedures. The remaining unprecipitated, unfixed components of the sample drop can then be washed out to the ring zone. Gaseous reagents are advantageous for fixation, because the danger of enlarging the original spot by dilution can be avoided.

A convenient glass apparatus[2] for effecting precipitations in a drop on filter paper is shown in Fig. 6. A wide-necked 50-ml glass flask carries a dropping funnel D and two glass tubes O and U with a plain ground flange of 10 mm ; the inner diameter of the glass tubes is 20 mm. The two flanges are held together by two spiral springs S or two rubber bands. The generator is connected to a water jet pump by the stopcock C_2 on the glass tube O. A small cotton plug is placed in the glass tube U to prevent acid droplets from being carried over with the air flow.

The most useful gaseous group precipitant is obviously hydrogen sulphide. The operation of the gas generator is shown by the following example of the precipitation of copper with hydrogen sulphide.

The glass flask contains zinc sulphide and the dropping funnel contains sulphuric acid (1:2). Alternative reagents can be used for producing hydrogen sulphide, e. g. barium sulphide with sulphuric acid, or aluminium sulphide with water. A spot of a copper sulphate solution is placed in the centre of a filter paper and the paper is inserted between the two flanges of the apparatus, so that it is centred in the opening of the glass tubes ; for this purpose it is only necessary to lift the upper glass tube O. The stopcock, C_1, is turned to allow a few drops of acid to fall on to the zinc sulphide, then the water jet pump is switched on and stopcock, C_2, is carefully opened so that hydrogen sulphide is drawn through the filter paper to precipitate the copper.

When high concentrations of precipitable metal ions are present, it is advisable to place a drop of alcohol on the spot and to repeat the precipitation with hydrogen sulphide. The drop of alcohol should be such that its diameter exceeds that of the original spot by about 1 mm; this can easily be achieved by using a capillary pipette. It is then easy to determine the effect of further hydrogen sulphide treatment in this outer zone, i. e. whether the precipitation is complete or not.

The whole precipitation procedure requires no more than three to five minutes, even if precipitation is repeated three times to ensure its completion.

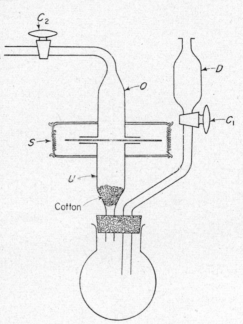

FIG. 6. The gas generator

In addition to the apparatus just described, any conventional gas generator can be used in conjunction with a glass flange arrangement (as shown in Fig. 6), in which the filter paper can be held. It should also be mentioned that in some cases it is sufficient to hold the paper over a bottle of hydrogen sulphide dissolved in water or acetone ; but this treatment does not always ensure quantitative precipitation. In general, a stream of the gaseous precipitant must be drawn *through* the paper.

C. The Sample Pipette and Glass Holder

To transfer the test drop to the filter paper, a self-filling capillary pipette[4] is used, so that drops of equal size are always produced. This is essential for comparison purposes and is especially important in applying the ring oven technique for semi-quantitative analysis as described later (chapter III, p. 69).

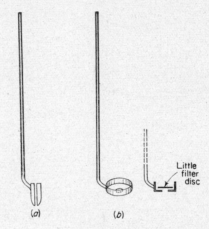

FIG. 7. (a) The capillary sample pipette
(b) The glass holder for the paper-disc

Fig. 7(a) illustrates such a capillary sample pipette, in which a conically tapered capillary tube is attached to a glass rod which serves as a holder. The length of this capillary is shorter than the capillary rise of the usual aqueous solutions in it ; hence it can easily be completely filled by merely dipping it into, or, better, touching it to the surface of, the sample solution. These pipettes are readily cleaned after use by filling them a few times with distilled water and alcohol.

The capacity of the pipettes obviously depends on the length and inner diameter of the capillary and in most cases described in this monograph, the sample pipettes have a capacity of about 1.5 μl. Pipettes of different capacity should also be available in the laboratory for special purposes.

The sample drop is transferred to the paper by placing the pipette on the marked centre of the filter paper ; the paper draws the sample drop out of the capillary. It is therefore essential to have close contact between the tip of the capillary and the paper and to ensure this, the tip of the capillary must be carefully rounded. This can easily be accomplished by grinding the water-filled capillary in a rough porcelain mortar. A similar rounded tip is also necessary for the pipette used in elution on the ring oven. Although these precautions may seem elaborate, experience has proved that their neglect may cause considerable difficulties.

Fig. 7(b) shows the glass holder[4] used in handling the small filter paper discs of 12 mm diameter which are punched out of the filter paper in the course of a systematic analysis (as described in the following chapter). This glass holder facilitates the treatment of a sample spot on the paper disc with gaseous reagents, for instance, fuming over hydrochloric acid or ammonia solution, or over bromine water for oxidation. To carry out these treatments, the disc containing the sample is simply held in the glass holder into a wide-necked glass bottle which contains the necessary reagent solution.

CHAPTER II

QUALITATIVE ANALYSIS

A. WITHOUT SEPARATIONS

IN microchemical analysis it is often necessary to carry out identification tests for several ions in but a single drop of test solution. Owing to the development of highly selective, or even specific reagents, and to present knowledge of masking of interfering ions, the analyst can frequently carry out identification reactions for several ions in presence of each other. However, even these reactions will be of little value if the volume of the test drop is so small that it cannot be divided to apply the various tests. As mentioned above, it is often impracticable to dilute the test drop. Obviously, the same considerations apply in cases where the single drop must be tested for one substance only with several reagents.

The ring oven can be used with great advantage in these cases. The test drop is placed on a round filter which is put on the ring oven and the components are washed into the ring zone with a suitable solvent. The filter is then dried and cut with scissors into as many sectors as are required for the various identification reactions. The separate tests are easily made on the individual sectors. The single drop is thus subdivided without dilution ; in fact, the concentration of the substances in the ring zone is even greater than in the original test drop, as was demonstrated in the previous chapter (p. 19).

It is of no significance for observation purposes whether a whole ring or only a part of it is developed with a particular reagent, because the colour of the line is uniformly intense. Thus, instead of one identification reaction in one test drop, several reactions can be carried out with higher sensitivities.

Moreover, the unused parts of the ring can be retained as required for record purposes.

B. SEPARATIONS

In the majority of cases it is advantageous to carry out separations before applying the different identification reactions. Either reagent solutions or gaseous precipitants can be used as precipitants for the groups of substances to be fixed. The following two examples illustrate the separation procedures.

(1) Separation into two groups

A model example is the separation of a mixture of copper, iron and nickel. It is best to precipitate, and fix, the copper with hydrogen sulphide ; iron and nickel, which are not precipitated, can then be eluted into the ring zone.

The test drop is placed in the centre of a round filter paper. The filter is inserted between the flanges of the gas generator and the copper is precipitated as copper sulphide (see p. 20). The paper is then placed on the ring oven. The iron and nickel are washed from the copper sulphide spot into the ring zone with $0.05N$ hydrochloric acid. The precipitate of copper sulphide can sometimes close the pores of the filter paper, particularly when the copper concentration is high, and this may make the elution process more difficult. It is thus advantageous to begin the extraction with one or two drops of ethanol and then continue the washing with $0.05N$ hydrochloric acid.

When all the soluble substances, i. e. iron and nickel, are collected in the ring zone (this takes 5—10 washings) the filter paper is dried.

There now exists between the inner spot containing the copper sulphide, and the outer ring containing the iron and nickel, a "neutral" zone, which is free of metal ions, hence it is possible to separate the copper sulphide mechanically by removing the inner spot with a punch (12 mm inner diameter) and a hammer ; this should be done on a paper-covered wooden base. Stainless steel punches are commercially available.

The remaining filter paper is cut into several sectors, in which the iron and nickel can be identified. The iron may be detected by spraying with 1 % potassium ferrocyanide solution, and the nickel by spraying with an alcoholic dimethylglyoxime solution (1 %). (Details of the identification reactions are given later on (pp. 39 and 40).

The punched filter disc contains the copper as copper sulphide which has to be converted to a soluble form. This is best accomplished by oxidation to copper sulphate ; the disc is fumed over bromine water with the aid of the glass holder (p. 22). The copper can then easily be detected directly on the disc, e.g. with α-benzoinoxime.

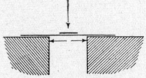

FIG. 8. Transfer of substances from the little disc into a second filter

When the dissolved precipitate on the disc contains several ions which are to be identified, these must be concentrated in a ring zone so that several identification reactions can be applied. The small filter disc is placed in the middle of another round filter and moistened with a drop of water, and the two filters are positioned on the ring oven so that the small disc lies just underneath the glass guide-tube. The washing procedure is then carried out in the normal manner with a suitable solvent, as previously described. The metal ions are dissolved, absorbed by the underlying filter and are finally collected in the ring zone. The ring can then be cut into several sectors for test purposes. Fig. 8 illustrates the process.

(2) Separation into three groups

It is also possible to divide a mixture of ions into more than two groups. An example is the analysis of a test drop containing lead, antimony, iron and nickel.

The sample drop on the filter paper is treated with hydrogen sulphide, as in the previous example, to precipitate lead and antimony. The iron and nickel are then washed into the ring zone with 0.05N hydrochloric acid. The inner spot which carries the sulphide precipitate is punched out of the dried filter. Iron and nickel are tested for on sectors of this first ring as described above.

The small disc is placed on another round filter for further separation. The filter and disc are placed on the ring oven and eluted with yellow ammonium sulphide. The antimony sulphide is dissolved, drawn into the underlying filter, and is then concentrated in the outer ring zone. After 10—15 washings, the separation of the antimony from the lead sulphide is complete, the latter remaining in the original spot on the disc. The filter and disc are dried, the lead sulphide is oxidized to lead sulphate by fuming over bromine water, and the lead is identified, e. g. with sodium rhodizonate. The ring zone contains the antimony as the sulphide and the antimony can be identified in a sector with an appropriate reagent. Sectors of the ring could be tested, if necessary, for any of the individual ions of this group such as arsenic, antimony, tin and molybdenum.

(3) Separation of substances already collected in a particular group

In most cases, there is no need for further separation of ions or substances which have been collected in a certain ring. If the precipitation reagents for fixation and the solvents for extracting the unprecipitated parts are correctly chosen, a suitable distribution of the substances contained in the sample drop can nearly always be accomplished. When proper separation steps are used, the ions appearing in any group should not interfere with the identification of the individual ions within the group. However, it may sometimes be advantageous to carry out additional separations of substances which have already been collected in one ring zone. The ease with which this can be done by the ring oven technique makes the method very flexible and suitable for practical applications.

Three different possibilities for such further separations which have been worked out are described below. The simplest method, which demands no additional equipment, enables further separation to be carried out on just a sector of the ring.

A suitable example is provided by a ring zone containing copper and iron as chlorides. A sector is cut out of the dried ring. Half of a round filter is placed on the ring oven and the sector containing the copper and iron is placed on this in such a way that its tip lies beneath the glass guide-tube and projects over the semicircular paper for some millimeters, as shown in Fig. 9(a).

The tip, A, of the filter paper represents the spot from which both the copper and iron were initially washed to the ring zone R_1. When a typical ring zone extraction is now performed

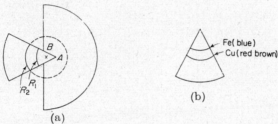

(a)

(b)

FIG. 9. Further separation of substances already collected in a ring zon

starting at point B, the soluble substances contained in ring R_1 are transported further outwards and form a second ring zone, R_2, which is nearly concentric with ring R_1 at a distance corresponding to the length A—B. The semicircular filter serves only as a support for the sector during this operation.

When this particular extraction is carried out with a mixture of ammonium hydroxide and ammonium chloride solution, only the copper is transported to ring R_2, because the iron is precipitated as hydroxide and thus fixed in ring R_1. The paper sector is dried, fumed over hydrochloric acid and sprayed with potassium ferrocyanide solution ; two arcs appear, as shown in Fig. 9(b), a blue one for the iron and a red-brown one for the copper. This is typical of the manner in which such separations are performed ; the second extraction solvent should be a reagent, or a mixture of reagents, which precipitates one component, so that the other components can be washed from the initial ring. Should either ring contain several ions or substances to be detected, the sector can be cut into even smaller sectors and the different identification reactions can be carried out on each sector.

A second technique for further separations[3] has been described in connection with the glass ring oven, (Chapter I, p. 17), but a similarly appropriate arrangement could be utilized with the conventional metal ring oven. A round thin ground-glass plate, measuring 55 mm in diameter, is placed in the Plexiglas ring P of the glass ring oven (Fig. 4). This glass plate has a central bore-hole of 12 mm diameter and, being in direct contact with the glass ring oven, has also a surface temperature of 105— 110° C. It is then, in fact, a ring oven with a bore-hole of only 12 mm diameter. Substances can thus be first concentrated in the inner ring zone (12 mm diameter) and, after the glass plate has been removed from the oven, are further separated by another extraction with a solvent which precipitates part of the substances in this inner ring and transports the other parts into the outer ring zone (22 mm diameter). This technique essentially makes two ring ovens with different bore-hole diameters out of one. By using a punch of 15 mm diameter, the two rings can be completely separated from each other and cut into several parts. Some interesting separations are thus possible, for not only the original spot but also the two rings can be punched out and analysed.

An acidic test drop containing lead, iron and zinc provides a good example. The spot is first treated with hydrogen sulphide to precipitate the lead ; the iron and zinc are then washed out on the ring oven with hydrochloric acid into the inner ring zone (12 mm diameter). After the inner glass plate has been removed, the zinc is washed into the outer ring zone (22 mm) with ammonia solution, the iron being precipitated in the inner ring zone as hydroxide. As a result, the filter paper contains lead in the inner spot, which is encircled by an inner ring containing the iron and by an outer one containing the zinc.

A third method[5] for separating ions which have already been collected in a ring utilizes the following technique. Although all the ring oven separations thus far described are accomplished by radial liquid flow from a central spot out to the hot ring zone, it is also possible to wash in the opposite direction radially from the outer ring zone into the middle of the paper. In this case the centre must be hot in order to concentrate the substances trans ferred from the outer zone to this spot.

A simple device, shown in Fig. 10, can be used to effect washing in the opposite direction. The glass plate has a central hole of 25 mm diameter. Two concentric glass rings are cemented around this borehole with a space between them to form a groove which holds the washing liquid. The diameter and height of these two glass rings should be such that when a filter paper with a diameter of 55 mm is placed on them, its edges can be pressed into the groove; about 3 mm of the filter paper should dip into the washing liquid. To accomplish this, the inner diameter of the outer glass ring should be 55 mm, i. e. equal to the diameter of the round filter or slightly greater. The paper is most

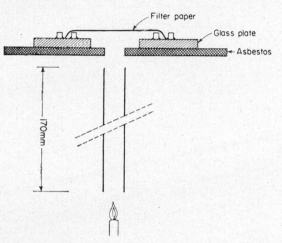

FIG. 10. Device for the "washing-in" technique

easily pressed into the groove with a glass ring of suitable dimensions. The glass plate is placed on an asbestos plate with a 10-mm hole and then held about 20 cm above a micro-burner flame so that the heat of the burner is transferred exactly to the centre of the hole by means of a glass tube which acts as a chimney. Any heating system could serve the same purpose if applied in an appropriate manner.

The use of this device may be shown by the example of a ring containing aluminium, iron, cobalt and nickel ; a separation into two groups, containing iron + aluminium and cobalt + nickel, respectively, is required. The ring is first fumed over ammonium hydroxide solution to precipitate the iron and the aluminium. The filter is placed centrally on the device described above and the edge of the paper is pressed into the groove which

is then filled with $0.01N$ ammonium chloride solution. The
liquid migrates towards the centre of the filter paper carrying
with it the unprecipitated cobalt and nickel. Because the central
area is hot, the water vaporizes leaving behind the dissolved
components so that after an interval of time all the cobalt and
nickel are concentrated in the central spot. This spot can then
be punched out of the dried filter and placed on another filter on
the ring oven and the ions can again be washed into a ring zone.
Identification reactions can be carried out for cobalt and nickel
on two sectors of the ring zone, and iron and aluminium can be
detected in sectors of the original ring.

The great advantage of this technique is that all the substances contained in a ring can, if necessary, be washed back into
the centre, so that a new separation can often be carried out on
the original paper. For example, in the case just described,
"washing-in" could be carried out with $0.05 N$ hydrochloric acid
which would transport all four ions back to the middle, whence
they could be further separated as required.

The three different methods of performing separations of
substances already concentrated in a ring are of considerable
value in special cases.

C. Systematic Schemes for the Analysis of Metal Ions

Despite the many excellent reagents which have been described in recent years, really specific reactions for every ion are
not available, and separations must normally be applied before
identification reactions are used in the course of a qualitative
analysis of a mixture of unknowns. Even if specific reactions
were available for all ions, a separation scheme might still be
preferable in many cases, particularly if the sample available
were very small. Dilution of the sample may be inadvisable
owing to insufficient sensitivity of the individual identification
reactions. Furthermore, the test drop may contain ions apart
from that being tested for, and the loss of these ions on discard-
ing the drop may not always be tolerable in microchemical analysis. Thus the separation of the ions contained in a mixture

into different groups may be desirable even when specific reactions are available.

Because the ring oven technique makes it possible to vary the group precipitation reagents (gas and liquid) and the extraction solvents (hydrochloric acid, ammonia solution, sodium hydroxide, etc.) and to combine them in various ways with different operations such as elution, punching or washing into a second filter, a large number of ions contained in a single drop can be divided into several groups and identified. Of course, care must be exercised to collect ions in such groups that they do not interfere with each other during identification ; but this is a necessary condition in any analytical scheme.

It should be emphasized here that the ring oven method is not paper chromatography, even though it is carried out on a paper and is occasionally referred to as "a special kind of paper chromatography". In paper chromatography separations are based on the different behaviour of the substances towards a solvent (or a solvent mixture) resulting in differential migration from a starting point ; the ring oven method uses the older and well-known methods of separation by chemical precipitation and the filtration processes take place horizontally.

The ring oven method can be used to work out analytical separation schemes for special purposes, for example, for the qualitative analysis of steel, of noble metals, and of non-ferrous alloys. In the present chapter are described three generally applicable analytical schemes for metal ions, which can be carried out in only one or two drops of solution ; these should be regarded as examples only and not as the limited field of application. The same principles and considerations can be used in many cases to work out various separation schemes. In practical analytical work the number of unknowns in a sample is rather limited and many ions can therefore be neglected right from the beginning, thus simplifying the schemes. The more common metal ions are included in the three cases to be described.

Because only one or two drops of solution are necessary for the application of any of the following schemes, the dissolution f a few micrograms of the solid samples can be effected very iickly by suitable acids (hydrochloric, nitric, sulphuric acid or aqua regia) or by a conventional fusion procedure with sodium carbonate, sodium peroxide, or sodium carbonate and potassium nitrate, etc.

A very simple but, nevertheless, efficient method of obtaining a metallic sample is the one described by Strebinger and Holzer[6] in which a microscope slide with a roughened section in its centre is rubbed several times across the specimen to be analysed. A few micrograms of the alloy — quite sufficient for analysis on the ring oven — thus produce a streak on the roughened glass surface. The effect on the specimen is hardly visible so that this sampling method is especially valuable in cases where no damage must be done to the object to be analysed, e. g. in art investigations. The streak on the glass surface can be dissolved very easily in a drop of acid, the solution can be evaporated to dryness, and the sample redissolved with an acid of the strength appropriate to the analysis.

Another very convenient method of sampling is provided by electrography, i. e., by anodic dissolution of the metal sample ; this is described in chapter IV (p. 87).

(1) The separation scheme for 14 metals[4]

This separation scheme deals with the following fourteen ions : lead, bismuth, copper, cadmium, tin, antimony, iron, nickel, cobalt, manganese, chromium, aluminium, zinc and titanium.

A single test drop is sufficient for the application of this scheme.

Place the test drop, which must not be more acidic than 1N in hydrochloric acid, in the middle of a filter paper (Schleicher-Schüll 589² or Whatman 40) by means of the self-filling capillary sampling pipette (p. 22), the drop volume being about 1.5 μl. It is advisable to mark the middle of the round filter with a pin before applying the test drop. All the following extraction procedures are carried out starting from this point.

Push the filter with the sample drop between the two flanges of the gas-generator (p. 21) and precipitate with hydrogen sulphide as described previously (p. 20). All the lead, bismuth, copper, cadmium, t and antimony are precipitated as sulphides and thus fixed in the c ginal spot. Repeat the precipitation after applying a drop of alcohol to the spot, in order to achieve complete fixation.

Place the filter on the hot ring oven so that the marked centre lies exactly under the capillary pipette. Wash all the soluble, unfixed metals into the outer ring zone with 0.05N hydrochloric acid (containing a little hydrogen sulphide solution) as described before (p. 17). It is advantageous to start the elution with a drop of alcohol and then to continue with the 0.05N hydrochloric acid (see p. 26). All the iron, nickel, cobalt, manganese, chromium, zinc, aluminium and titanium are thus concentrated in the ring.

Dry the filter paper, preferably by means of a hot air drier, and punch out the inner spot with a 12-mm punch using a hammer on a piece of paper-covered wood. The small disc contains all the lead, bismuth, antimony, tin, copper and cadmium as sulphides, whereas the remaining filter carries the other eight metals and is called RING I. The ions contained in RING I need not be separated further because decisive identification is possible for each ion of this group.

Moisten the punched-out disc with a drop of alcohol and oxidize with bromine vapour ; to do this, hold it over the mouth of a wide-necked bottle containing bromine water, in the glass holder (p. 22). After the oxidation, fume the filter disc thoroughly over ammonia solution. If the oxidation is incomplete, which can easily be judged by the colour of the spot, repeat the treatment with bromine vapour and ammonia. Then dry the disc to fix the antimony and tin. Tin hydroxide, in particular, tends to precipitate in such a fine dispersion that it may migrate with ammonia solution during the next extraction step ; this can be avoided by drying the disc. The disc then contains lead as sulphate, copper and cadmium as their tetrammine complexes, and antimony, tin and bismuth as hydroxides or basic salts.

After the little disc has been dried, place it on a new round filter and wash it on the ring oven with dilute ammonium hydroxide solution. The copper and cadmium are dissolved, sucked into the underlying filter and then concentrated in the ring zone. Lead sulphate, bismuth, tin and antimony hydroxides or basic salts are insoluble in ammoniacal solution and remain in the disc. This mode of separation is preferable to the more usual one involving ammonium sulphide, which is, however, applied in another stage of this scheme, because much of the copper sulphide would be soluble in ammonium sulphide.

Dry the filter and disc ; the filter contains the copper and cadmium in a sharply outlined zone and is called RING II.

Again place the filter disc, where the lead, bismuth, tin and antimony remain in the original spot, on the centre of a fresh filter and place together on the ring oven. Wash the tin and antimony into the ring zone with yellow ammonium sulphide. After applying several drops of ammonium sulphide, complete the elution with dilute ammonium hydroxide solution. Dry the filter and disc. The disc contains the lead and bismuth again as their sulphides in the original spot, which still has the same size and shape as at the beginning of the analysis. The filter itself contains all the antimony and tin as sulphides in the sharply defined ring zone ; this is named Ring III.

All ions have now been separated into such groups that individual identification is possible. The whole procedure, which requires only one drop of about 1.5 μl, takes less than 15 minutes.

The whole scheme is summarized in Table 1.

Table 1. Separation Scheme (II C 1)

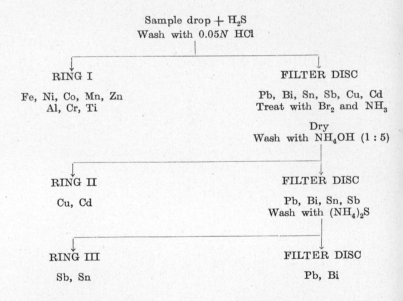

Sample drop + H_2S
Wash with 0.05N HCl

RING I

Fe, Ni, Co, Mn, Zn
Al, Cr, Ti

FILTER DISC

Pb, Bi, Sn, Sb, Cu, Cd
Treat with Br_2 and NH_3

Dry
Wash with NH_4OH (1 : 5)

RING II

Cu, Cd

FILTER DISC

Pb, Bi, Sn, Sb
Wash with $(NH_4)_2S$

RING III

Sb, Sn

FILTER DISC

Pb, Bi

Identification Reactions

The various ions separated into the four groups can now be identified. All the identification reactions are carried out directly on the paper without further extraction because loss of test material and dilution of the substances which are already concentrated in sharp lines are thus avoided. Moreover, the application of spot reactions directly on the paper is the easiest and most convenient method of identification. Identification reactions should be carried out in such a way that the ions which are concentrated in defined rings do not diffuse, hence only reactions which rapidly produce insoluble coloured precipitates should be applied. This is possible in all cases except that of antimony where no sufficiently reliable direct identification reaction exists. The choice of the identification reactions which are described below is to a certain extent governed by personal preference, but in most cases the possibilities are limited by the above considerations. Future developments in spot analysis will probably produce better reactions with a higher degree of sensitivity. In many cases well-known identification reactions had to be modified to cope with the conditions encountered.

For fuller details of most of the reactions described in the following pages, the reader should consult *Spot Tests in Inorganic Analysis* by Fritz Feigl (5th ed., 1958, Elsevier, Amsterdam).

Lead

All the lead is found together with the bismuth as sulphide in the original spot on the small disc.

Oxidize by fuming the disc over bromine water and then over ammonia solution using the glass holder (Fig. 7(b), p. 22), and quickly dry the disc to remove the excess bromine. The lead sulphide is thus oxidized to lead sulphate. Spot with a drop of freshly prepared 0.2% aqueous solution of sodium rhodizonate. Fume over hydrochloric acid until the yellow colour of the reagent disappears. A violet to red spot indicates the presence of lead.[7]

Bismuth

Bismuth can be identified in the same spot as the lead, after the above test.

Fume the filter disc first over bromine and then over ammonia solution to destroy the rhodizonic acid, which is indicated by the disappearance of colour. Place the disc on a spot plate or watch-glass, spot with a drop of hydrogen peroxide solution (5%) and heat in a drying oven to destroy any sulphide still present which might interfere with the test for bismuth ; this heating also removes excess of hydrogen peroxide. Add a drop of saturated lead chloride solution followed by two drops of a strongly alkaline freshly prepared stannite solution. If bismuth is present, a black precipitate appears. Particularly if small amounts are to be detected, carry out a blank test.

The principle of this reaction is that lead is not normally reduced by stannite solution in the cold but the rapid reduction of bismuth induces the reduction of lead ; therefore, the reaction is visible even if very small amounts of bismuth are present.[8]

Tin

All the tin in the test drop is contained with the antimony as sulphide in Ring III.

Cut out a sector of this ring on which the circular line is easily visible. Oxidize the tin sulphide with a 1 : 1 mixture of a 10% hydrogen peroxide solution and ammonium hydroxide solution. To maintain the narrow line of tin sulphide, conduct the oxidation in the following way. Fill a very fine glass capillary with the oxidation mixture and run the capillary rapidly over the streak on the paper, using it as a pen so that only a very narrow moistened line is obtained. All the tin is thus converted to the hydroxide. Then spray with (or dip in) a 0.02% solution of morin (pentahydroxyflavanol) in acetone and finally bathe on a watch-glass in a solution of 5 ml of acetic acid in 100 ml of ethanol to remove excess of the reagent. A yellow-green fluorescent line of tin morinate in ultraviolet light indicates tin.[9]

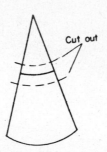

FIG. 11. Dissection of the circular arc

Antimony

Another sector of Ring III is used for the detection of antimony.

Dissect the circular arc as closely as possible from the sector as shown in Fig. 11, and place it on a spot plate. Add 1—2 drops of hydrochloric acid (1 : 1) to dissolve antimony sulphide, followed by a drop of 5% potassium iodide solution and a crystal of sodium hydrogen sulphite to reduce the antimony. Mix by blowing with a pipette, add a drop of 0.5% rhodamine B solution and mix again. If antimony is present, a blue-violet precipitate appears. Carry out a blank test.[10, 11]

The identification of antimony can also be carried out by an alternative procedure. Place the filter strip with the antimony sulphide in a micro-test-tube, dissolve the sulphide with 5 drops of sulphuric acid (1 : 3), add a crystal of sodium hydrogen sulphite and a drop of 10% potassium iodide solution, and mix. Then extract the antimony with an equal volume of benzene. Separate the two layers and place the benzene solution on a spot plate. A drop of 0.2% rhodamine B solution again produces the blue-violet precipitate if antimony is present.[12]

Copper

A sector of RING II, which contains all the copper and cadmium, is used.

Fume over ammonia and spray with a 1% alcoholic solution of dithiooxamide (rubeanic acid). An olive green to black line of copper rubeanate indicates copper.[13]

Alternatively, identify copper by spraying with an alcoholic solution of a-benzoin-oxime and fuming over ammonia. A yellow-green line indicates copper.[14]

Cadmium

Another sector of RING II is required for this test.

Moisten with a solution of hydrogen sulphide in acetone to precipitate all the cadmium (and copper) as sulphides. Rinse the sector thoroughly under the tap and if copper is known to be present, rinse it in a 1% solution of potassium cyanide to dissolve all the copper sulphide. After rinsing a yellow line of cadmium sulphide is visible.[15] In order to make this line more distinct, bathe the sector in a 1% silver nitrate solution. Instead of the yellow line of cadmium sulphide, an equivalent dark brown to black line of silver sulphide appears if cadmium is present.

Iron

The iron is contained together with nickel, cobalt, chromium, manganese, zinc, aluminium and titanium in RING I.

Fume a sector of this ring over hydrochloric acid and then oxidize over bromine water to convert any iron reduced by the hydrogen sulphide treatment. Spray with a 1% aqueous solution of potassium ferrocyanide. A distinct blue line appears if iron is present.

Cobalt

Another sector of RING I is required.

Fume over ammonium hydroxide solution and moisten with a 5% solution of disodium hydrogen phosphate ; this forms ferric phosphate and cobalt phosphate and the iron is thus masked. Treat with a 1% solution of a-nitroso-β-naphthol in acetone. Cobalt forms a brown-red precipitate.[16]

Nickel

Another sector of RING I is used.

Fume over ammonium hydroxide solution and spray with a 1% solution of dimethylglyoxime in ethanol. A red line indicates nickel.[17]

If much ferric hydroxide accompanies the nickel precipitate, the recognition of the red nickel dimethylglyoxime colour may be difficult. In this case, bathe the sector finally in a solution of potassium tartrate which dissolves the red-brown iron(III) hydroxide, leaving behind the nickel dimethylglyoxime.

Chromium

Another sector of RING I is used for the identification of chromium.

Oxidize the chromium to chromate with hydrogen peroxide-ammonia solution using the capillary as described in the test for tin (p. 38). To ensure complete oxidation as well as to destroy the excess hydrogen peroxide, dry the sector in a drying oven, spray with a freshly prepared 1% solution of diphenylcarbazide in ethanol and finally dip into 2N sulphuric acid. A violet line denotes chromium.[18]

Manganese

Another sector of RING I is taken.

Spray with an ammoniacal silver nitrate solution and warm. A dark brown to black line of finely dispersed metallic silver and manganese dioxide indicates manganese.[19]

If cobalt is known to be absent, the identification of manganese may also be carried out with benzidine. Moisten the sector with 0.05N potassium hydroxide solution and then spray with a 0.05% acetic acid solution of benzidine. A blue line indicates manganese.[20]

Zinc

For the identification of the zinc, the mutual precipitation of zinc and cobalt with ammonium mercury thiocyanate[21] is used but the technique is modified to meet the particular conditions here. In very dilute solutions (0.02%) cobalt precipitates only very slowly, but if zinc is also present, the cobalt mercury thiocyanate comes down quickly.

Moisten a sector of RING I with ammonium mercury thiocyanate solution (3.3 g of ammonium thiocyanate and 3 g of mercuric chloride dissolved in 5 ml of water without warming). Then draw the sector several times through a few drops of a 0.02% solution of cobalt sulphate on a watch-glass. Where zinc is present, i. e. in the circular arc, blue cobalt mercury thiocyanate is formed. Any blue spots appearing on other parts of the paper can be ignored. It should be emphasized that iron does not interfere with this reaction because iron(III) thiocyanate is soluble, whereas the blue cobalt mercury thiocyanate precipitates.

Aluminium

RING I again provides the necessary sector.

Spray with a saturated solution of morin in methanol, dry and rinse in 2N hydrochloric acid to remove the excess of reagent as well as other morinates. Place under ultraviolet light while still moist. A yellow-green fluorescent line indicates aluminium.[22]

Titanium

Treat another sector of RING I with a 5% aqueous solution of chromotropic acid. A red-brown line indicates titanium.[23]

Iron(III) produces a green compound but this does not normally interfere with the test because it appears only on the outer edges of the line. If high iron concentrations are present, any interference can be avoided by treating the developed sector with stannous chloride solution ; the iron(II) does not react with chromotropic acid.

Table 2 summarizes the reactions which are used in this particular separation scheme.

The entire analysis, including separation and identification, takes less than one hour. It should be noted that not even the whole amount of sample contained in the single drop is actually used. The unused parts of the different rings (only two sectors of RING II and RING III are required, for example) can be retained for record purposes ; confirmatory reactions can be carried out on the remaining parts of the ring if necessary.

If the test solution is very dilute, several drops should be used for analysis. If more than 5—6 test drops are used, the paper should be dried between the addition of the drops in order to keep the spot to a reasonable size.

With respect to the amount of sample and the sensitivity of this analytical scheme, it should be noted that there must be at least as much present of every ion in the sample drop as would be necessary to test for this particular ion separately in a ring. Therefore, the amount of sample required depends on the ion which is present in the lowest concentration.

It is not possible to say more about the sensitivity in general terms because the identification limits of the various reactions are different ; moreover, the identification limits are also influenced by the presence of other ions in the group. Thus the sample

Table 2. IDENTIFICATION REACTIONS

	Element	Pretreatment	Reaction	Colour
DISC	Pb	fume over Br_2, then over NH_4OH	Sodium rhodizonate	blue-violet-red
	Bi	on spot plate + H_2O_2, heat	$PbCl_2 + Na_2SnO_2 + NaOH$	black
RING III	Sn	$H_2O_2 + NH_4OH$	Morin, alcoholic CH_3COOH	yellow-green fluorescent in U.V.
	Sb	on spot plate + HCl(1 : 1)	KI, SO_3^{2-} Rhodamine B	blue violet
RING II	Cu	fume over NH_4OH	Dithiooxamide (rubeanic acid)	olive green-black
	Cd		$S^{2-}, + KCN, + AgNO_3$	black
RING I	Fe	fume over HCl, Br_2	$K_4[Fe(CN)_6]$	blue
	Co	fume over NH_4OH	$Na_2HPO_4, + a$-nitroso--β-naphthol	red-brown
	Ni	fume over NH_4OH	Dimethylglyoxime	red
	Cr	$H_2O_2 + NH_4OH$	Diphenylcarbazide + H_2SO_4	violet
	Mn		$[Ag(NH_3)_2]^+ + NH_4OH$	black
	Mn		+ NaOH + Benzidine	blue
	Zn		$[Hg(CNS)_4]^{2-} + Co^{2+}$	blue
	Al		Morin	yellow-green fluorescent in U.V.
	Ti		Chromotropic acid	red-brown

amounts are defined not by the separation operation but by the identification limits of the various reactions.

If, for example, a 1.5 μl test drop containing 30 μg of solid undergoes separation, as little as 1 % of the solid can be detected after suitable separation provided that the identification limit of the reaction used is better than 0.3 μg ; most of the reactions used easily fulfil this condition.

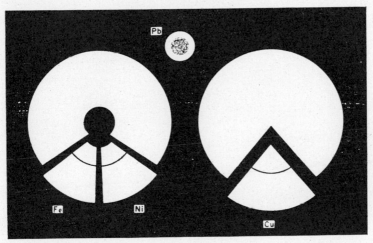

FIG. 12. Analysis of a 1.5 μl sample drop (Pb, Cu, Fe, Ni)

The sensitivity of the scheme detailed above is shown by an analysis of a total of 1.5 μg of copper, iron, nickel, and lead in 1.5 μl of solution. Figure 12 illustrates the results ; iron and nickel have been developed on two sectors of RING I, while copper has been identified in RING II. The original spot shows lead rhodizonate. Because the sample did not contain antimony or tin, there was no need to develop RING III. The large unused parts of the two rings should be noted.

It is possible to extend the scheme to cover other ions. Bank and Van der Eijk[24] included mercury and arsenic. The mercury remains throughout the separation with the lead and bismuth on the filter disc, where it is finally detected in half of the spot with stannous chloride and aniline. Arsenic is washed with ammonium carbonate solution into the ring zone before tin and antimony are extracted with ammonium sulphide ; the arsenic is detected by the Gutzeit test.

In another extension, Stephen[25] washes beryllium, zirconium potassium and magnesium into RING I, where they can be identified by one of the usual reactions. Stephen has also suggested testing for mercury (I) and silver in a separate test drop by precipitating both ions as the chlorides. The rest of the sample is washed out, the chloride spot is punched out and after the ions have been transferred to another filter, they are separated with ammonia solution ; the silver forms a ring, while the mercury remains in the centre spot as black $Hg(NH_2) Cl \cdot Hg$.

(2) The separation scheme using "washing out" and "washing in" techniques[5]

The method of transporting ions already concentrated in a ring zone back into the centre spot by radial washing, as described previously (p. 31), can be used to carry out complete separation schemes. The possibility of such further separations enhances considerably the flexibility of the ring oven method. The following separation scheme illustrates the procedure.

Spot the test drop on the centre of a 55 mm filter paper and treat with hydrogen sulphide. Wash the unprecipitated ions into the ring zone with $0.1N$ hydrochloric acid. Dry the paper and punch out the inner spot carrying the sulphide precipitate. Separate the sulphide group metals (lead, bismuth, copper, cadmium, tin, antimony) as described on p. 35. Cut out the ring in a circular band 10 mm wide ; treat this filter paper ring (12 mm inner diameter, 32 mm outer diameter) which contains all the other metal ions concentrated in the circular line, with a 3% hydrogen peroxide and $1N$ ammonium hydroxide solution. Dry the ring and place it on a fresh filter paper. Place the whole on to the glass apparatus shown in Fig. 10 (p. 31) and press the edge of the paper into the round groove which contains $0.01N$ ammonium chloride solution. The cobalt, nickel, zinc, part of the chromium and magnanese, and barium, strontium, calcium and magnesium are thus transferred to the warmed centre of the supporting filter ; this takes about 20 minutes. Aluminium, iron and part of chromium and manganese remain in the first ring where they can be identified in the different sectors.

Dry the paper, punch out the inner spot, fume it over ammonia, place on another filter and treat with hydrogen sulphide. All the cobalt, nickel, manganese, zinc and chromium are thus fixed, whilst the alkaline earth metals are unprecipitated. Place the filter with the little disc on the ring oven and transport all the alkaline earth metals to the ring zone with $0.1N$ acetic acid. Identify the different metals in sectors of this ring, e. g. microscopically after extraction, or by spot reactions.

Oxidize the metal sulphides on the little disc with bromine vapour and ammonia, place the disc on another filter and wash the five metal ions again into the ring zone with $0.1N$ acetic acid. Dry the paper and identify the metals in the usual way.

The above scheme is summarized in Table 3.

Table 3. SEPARATION SCHEME (II C 2)

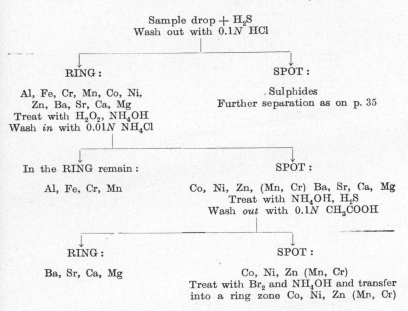

Sample drop + H_2S
Wash out with $0.1N$ HCl

RING :
Al, Fe, Cr, Mn, Co, Ni,
Zn, Ba, Sr, Ca, Mg
Treat with H_2O_2, NH_4OH
Wash *in* with $0.01N$ NH_4Cl

SPOT :
Sulphides
Further separation as on p. 35

In the RING remain :
Al, Fe, Cr, Mn

SPOT :
Co, Ni, Zn, (Mn, Cr) Ba, Sr, Ca, Mg
Treat with NH_4OH, H_2S
Wash *out* with $0.1N$ CH_3COOH

RING :
Ba, Sr, Ca, Mg

SPOT :
Co, Ni, Zn (Mn, Cr)
Treat with Br_2 and NH_4OH and transfer
into a ring zone Co, Ni, Zn (Mn, Cr)

(3) Separation scheme using liquid-liquid extraction procedures

Although the previous separation schemes are based on classical chemical methods of precipitation and filtration, liquid-liquid extraction methods can also be used to separate metallic ions into groups. Solvent extraction methods provide a rapid and easy method of separation.

The ring oven method permits the use of extremely small quantities of substance ; therefore it is only necessary to extract very small volumes, i. e. one or two drops, of the unknown aqueous solution.

West and Mukherji[26] describe a scheme for the separation of 35 metallic ions contained in one or two drops, based on a combination of liquid-liquid extraction and the ring oven technique. Both chelate extraction and ion association extraction (Morrison and Freiser)[27] are employed. The separation of the aqueous layer and the organic layer (volume approximately 2 ml) is carried out very conveniently with the help of the extraction pipette as described by Carlton[28] (Fig. 13).

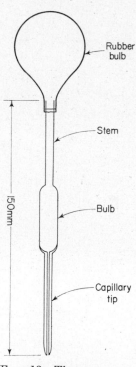

Rubber bulb

Stem

150mm

Bulb

Capillary tip

FIG. 13. The extraction pipette

The general procedure is to extract one or two drops of the aqueous solution with an organic solvent in the presence of suitable ion association or chelating agents under appropriate conditions of pH. The two layers are allowed to equilibrate in a test-tube and are then separated by the extraction pipette. At least three extractions are required to obtain the maximum efficiency of separation. Only the first extract need be used for the detection of the metallic ions, the others being discarded. The aqueous layer is then treated with other chelating or ion association reagents and again extracted, the separation processes being applied as necessary. The first extract of each group is transferred to the centre of a round filter with a capillary pipette through the glass guide-tube and the ions are washed into the ring zone with $0.1N$ hydrochloric acid. The filter is dried and cut into as many sectors as required. The various ions are then detected using spot test methods.

The 35 metallic ions are thus separated into five groups, contained in four organic extracts and the residual aqueous layer. The aqueous layer is also finally washed into the ring zone. The complete scheme including separations and identifications takes about one hour.

The general outline of the scheme is shown in Table 4.

Table 4. SEPARATION SCHEME:
LIQUID-LIQUID EXTRACTION (II C 3)

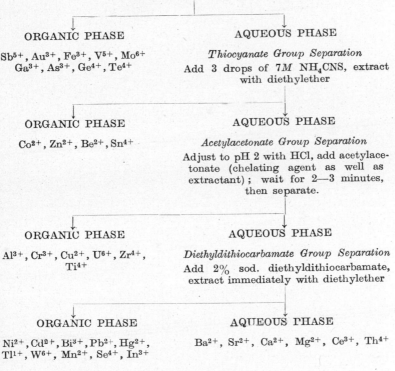

Chloride Group Separation

Test solution, adjust with conc. HCl to 7N. Extract with methylisobutyl ketone and n-amyl acetate (2 : 1)

ORGANIC PHASE

Sb^{5+}, Au^{3+}, Fe^{3+}, V^{5+}, Mo^{6+}
Ga^{3+}, As^{3+}, Ge^{4+}, Te^{4+}

AQUEOUS PHASE

Thiocyanate Group Separation

Add 3 drops of 7M NH_4CNS, extract with diethylether

ORGANIC PHASE

Co^{2+}, Zn^{2+}, Be^{2+}, Sn^{4+}

AQUEOUS PHASE

Acetylacetonate Group Separation

Adjust to pH 2 with HCl, add acetylacetonate (chelating agent as well as extractant); wait for 2—3 minutes, then separate.

ORGANIC PHASE

Al^{3+}, Cr^{3+}, Cu^{2+}, U^{6+}, Zr^{4+}, Ti^{4+}

AQUEOUS PHASE

Diethyldithiocarbamate Group Separation

Add 2% sod. diethyldithiocarbamate, extract immediately with diethylether

ORGANIC PHASE

Ni^{2+}, Cd^{2+}, Bi^{3+}, Pb^{2+}, Hg^{2+}, Tl^{1+}, W^{6+}, Mn^{2+}, Se^{4+}, In^{3+}

AQUEOUS PHASE

Ba^{2+}, Sr^{2+}, Ca^{2+}, Mg^{2+}, Ce^{3+}, Th^{4+}

D. REACTIONS FOR METAL IONS

It has been repeatedly mentioned that identification reactions must be carried out in the ring oven technique in such a way that the material concentrated in a sharp line does not become diffused. It is therefore very often necessary to modify well-known reactions, e. g. by a change in the order of addition of the reagents required. Adjustment of acidity and alkalinity should be carried out as far as possible by fuming over the appropriate reagent rather than by applying solutions directly to the paper. Oxidations and reductions should also be performed with gaseous reagents.

Although the mode of carrying out an identification test may often seem obvious, it ought to be verified experimentally to prove that sharp lines can be obtained. The reactions for metal ions which are described on the following pages have been thoroughly checked from this point of view. The reactions have been selected from those which have been used so far in the identification or semi-quantitative determination of metal ions collected in a ring zone. Statements about the selectivity or specificity of the various reactions are beyond the scope of this monograph. For more details and interferences of most of these tests, Feigl's *Spot Tests* should be consulted.

With regard to the purity of the reagents used, the ring oven method has certain advantages over more conventional methods of qualitative analysis. The essence of the technique is that after the separation process and the division of the paper, the identification reactions are carried out on individual sectors of the ring zone. Only reaction products in the sharply defined line are of significance. This is an obvious advantage, for coloured stains on other parts of the paper are of no significance and cannot be confused with the sharp line. If one of the identification test reagents should be contaminated, any interfering substances which it contained would, of course, never form a circular line. Thus, serious contamination can only occur in the reagents used to wash the rings and in the paper, for contamination from either source would end up in the ring zone. It is therefore advisable to test both paper and wash liquids for contaminants. The easiest way to do this is to carry out blank tests. The use of quantitative grade filter paper and pure analytical reagents avoids these problems in nearly all cases. For a discussion of the quality of filter papers and purification of wash liquid, see Chapter II, p. 67.

The numbers before each reaction refer to Table 5. (p. 57) where some information on sensitivities is given.

Silver

(1) Fume the ring zone over nitric acid and spray with a saturated solution of *p*-dimethylaminobenzylidenerhodanine in acetone. A red-violet colour indicates silver.[25, 29]

(2) Spray the ring zone with a 1% solution of potassium chromate. A red-brown line appears if silver is present.

(3) Fume the sector over hydrochloric acid and then treat with a 1% solution of manganese nitrate and a $0.1N$ sodium hydroxide solution. A black line indicates silver.[30]

(4) Spray the sector with a saturated solution of hydrogen sulphide in acetone. A dark-brown to black line of silver sulphide develops.

(5) Spray the sector with a freshly prepared 1% solution of stannous chloride, fume over ammonia solution and warm slightly. A black line of metallic silver appears on the paper.[31]

Mercury

(6) Fume the sector briefly over ammonia solution and heat ; then spray with a 1% solution of diphenylcarbazide in ethanol and dry. A violet-blue line denotes mercury.[32]

(7) Treat the sector with a freshly prepared stannous chloride solution followed by a drop of aniline, and warm, e.g. on a hot plate ; finally, rinse well under the tap. A black line remains if mercury is present.[33]

(8) Spray the sector with a very dilute solution of dithizone in chloroform and dry. An orange line develops if mercury is present.[34]

(9) Bathe the sector in a 1 : 1 mixture of a saturated alcoholic solution of *p*-dimethylaminobenzylidenerhodanine and a saturated aqueous solution of sodium acetate. A violet line indicates mercury.[25, 35]

Lead

(10) Bathe the sector in sodium sulphate solution and rinse well under the tap ; this fixes the lead as its sulphate. Then spray with a freshly prepared aqueous sodium rhodizonate solution and fume over hydrochloric acid. A red, violet or blue line appears depending on the pH ; all three colours are seen in succession during the fuming over hydrochloric acid.[7]

(11) Fix the lead in the circular arc as lead sulphate by dipping into sodium sulphate solution, then oxidize by bathing the sector in a 1 : 1 mixture of 3% hydrogen peroxide and concentrated ammonia solution ;

finally spray with a solution of benzidine in dilute acetic acid. A blue line indicates lead.[32]

Instead of benzidine, dimethylnaphthidine or diphenybenzidine can be used.

Bismuth

(12) Spray the sector with a cinchonine-potassium iodide solution (1 g of cinchonine in 100 ml of water containing a few drops of nitric acid and 2 g of potassium iodide). An orange-red line appears if bismuth is present.[36]

(13) Treat the sector with a freshly prepared 1% alkaline solution of stannite, spray with a 0.1% solution of a lead salt and dry. A black line indicates bismuth.[8] (See also p. 37.)

(14) The test described in 13. can be carried out without addition of lead solution but the sensitivity is then lower.[37]

Copper

(15) Test with dithio-oxamide, as described on p. 39.

(16) Fume the sector over ammonia solution, spray with a 1% solution of benzoinoxime, again fume over ammonia solution and dry. A green line appears if copper is present.[14]

(17) Spray the sector with a solution consisting of 0.2 g of o-tolidine and 1 g of ammonium thiocyanate in 10 ml of acetone. A blue line indicates copper.[38]

(18) Dip the sector into or spray it with a saturated solution of hydrogen sulphide in acetone, dry, rinse well under the tap to remove the excess of reagent, and bathe in a 1% solution of silver nitrate. A black line of silver sulphide appears if copper is present.

(19) Fume the sector over hydrochloric acid and spray with a saturated solution of 2.2'-diquinolyl (Cuproin) in alcohol which contains a few drops of water and a few crystals of hydroxylamine to reduce the copper. A purple-red cuprous complex appears.[39]

(20) This test is an example of an identification not directly carried out on the paper. Cut the line bearing the copper out of the sector, place on a spot plate, add a drop of a red ferric thiocyanate solution, and after a few seconds add 2 drops of a $0.1N$ sodium thiosulphate solution. The copper catalyses the reduction of the ferric ion by the thiosulphate, while the thiocyanate acts as indicator. Carry out a blank test at the same time with a similar strip of filter paper. If copper is present, the drop is decolorized quicker than the blank.[40]

Cadmium

(21) Bathe the sector in a saturated solution of ferrous dipyridyl iodide. A red line indicates cadmium.[25, 41]

(22) Spray the circular arc with an alcoholic solution of Cadion which contains sodium hydroxide. A pinkish red line denotes cadmium.[42]

(23) Detect the cadmium as silver sulphide, as described in test 18 for copper.

Arsenic

(24) This is another example of a test not carried out on the paper. Cut out the line containing the arsenic, and transfer to a micro-test-tube. Add a grain of metallic zinc and 1 or 2 drops of dilute sulphuric acid ; place a piece of filter paper impregnated with a 50% silver nitrate solution over the mouth of the tube. A yellow spot develops on the paper, which turns black on adding a droplet of water (Gutzeit test).[24]

Antimony

(25) Test with rhodamine B as described on p. 38 (See Table 2).

Tin

(26) Test with morin (pentahydroxyflavanol) as described on p. 38. (See also Table 2.)

Molybdenum

(27) Spray the sector with a 5% solution of stannous chloride in $3N$ hydrochloric acid and then with a 10% solution of potassium thiocyanate. A brick-red line of the molybdenum(III)-hexathiocyanato-complex appears.[43]

(28) Treat the sector with a 1:2 mixture of phenylhydrazine and acetic acid. A deep red line indicates molybdenum.[44]

Tungsten

(29) Spray the circular arc with a freshly prepared stannous chloride solution in 1:1 hydrochloric acid. A blue line denotes tungsten.[45]

(30) Dip the sector into a 0.1% solution of rhodamine B in $6N$ hydrochloric acid and then rinse well under running water. A violet line forms if tungsten is present.[43]

Vanadium

(31) Treat the circular arc on the sector with a 1:1 mixture of aniline and hydrochloric acid, thus forming a dark blue line of "aniline black".[46]

(32) Spray the sector with a mixture consisting of equal parts of a 3% hydrogen peroxide solution, water and concentrated sulphuric acid. A pink line appears which soon becomes diffuse.[47]

Gold

(33) Spray the sector with a 0.05% solution of benzidine in dilute acetic acid. A blue line results if gold is present.[48]

(34) Spray the sector with a saturated solution of *p*-dimethylamino-benzylidenerhodanine in acetone. A violet line indicates gold.[49]

Platinum

(35) Fix the platinum in the ring zone by spraying with a saturated thallium nitrate solution, wash with dilute ammonia solution and finally rinse under the tap. Spray with a freshly prepared stannous chloride solution in strong hydrochloric acid. A yellow to orange line develops.[50]

Cobalt

(36) Test with α-nitroso-β-naphthol as described on p. 39. (See also Table 2.)

(37) Fume the sector over ammonia solution and spray with a 1% solution of dithio-oxamide (rubeanic acid) in ethanol. A brown line indicates cobalt.[51]

(38) Spray the sector with a saturated solution of ammonium thio-cyanate in acetone and dry. A blue-green line indicates cobalt.[52]

Nickel

(39) Test with dimethylglyoxime as described on p. 40. (See also Table 2.) It is also possible to use the water-soluble nioxime, 1 : 2 cyclohexanedione dioxime.

(40) Fume the sector over ammonia solution and spray with a 1% solution of dithio-oxamide (rubeanic acid) in ethanol. A violet line indicates nickel.[51]

Iron

(41) Test with potassium ferrocyanide as described on p. 39. (See also Table 2.)

(42) Spray the sector with a 0.1% aqueous solution of potassium thiocyanate. A red line indicates iron.

(43) Spray the sector with a 2% solution of α-α'-dipyridyl in thio-glycolic acid and warm. The iron(III) is reduced by the thioglycolic acid to iron(II), which forms a pink complex cation with α-α'-dipyridyl.[53]

(44) Spray the sector with a 0.1 aqueous solution of 8-hydroxy-quinoline-7-iodo-5-sulphonic acid (Ferron). A green line appears if iron(III) is present.[54]

Chromium

(45) Test with diphenylcarbazide as described on p. 40. (See also Table 2.)

Manganese

(46) Treat the sector with $0.05N$ sodium hydroxide solution, rinse with water and spray with a saturated solution of 3 : 3'-dimethyl-naphthidine in $0.1N$ hydrochloric acid. A purple line indicates manganese.[25]

(47) Test with benzidine as described on p. 40. (See also Table 2.)

(48) Test with silver ammine solution as described on p. 40. (See also Table 2.)

Zinc

(49) Treat the ring zone on the sector with a 1% potassium ferricyanide solution, using a capillary as described in the test for tin (see p. 38). Treat the zone similarly with a saturated solution of 3 : 3'-dimethyl-naphthidine in $1N$ hydrochloric acid and finally wash with distilled water. A purple line denotes zinc.[25, 55]

(50) Test by mutual precipitation of zinc and cobalt with mercury thiocyanate as described on p. 40. (See also Table 2.)

Aluminium

(51) Test with morin, as described on p. 41. (See also Table 2.)

(52) Spray the sector with a 0.1% aqueous solution of aluminon and rinse well under the tap. A dark red line appears if aluminium is present.[56]

(53) Spray the sector with a 0.1% solution of alizarin S containing some ammonia solution ; after 10—20 seconds, spot with acetic acid (1 : 2) and rinse well under the tap. A red line appears.[57]

Beryllium

(54) Spray the sector with a 0.05% solution of 1 : 2 : 5 : 8-tetra-hydroxyanthraquinone (quinalizarin) in $0.1N$ sodium hydroxide. A purple red line appears if beryllium is present.[25, 58]

(55) Treat the sector with a saturated solution of the sodium salt of ethylenediaminetetra-acetic acid in ammonia solution (1 : 5) and then spray with a saturated alcoholic solution of morin. After drying, a yellow-green fluorescent line is visible under the quartz lamp.[59]

Titanium

(56) Test with chromotropic acid as described on p. 41. (See also Table 2.)[60]

Zirconium

(57) Spray the sector with a 0.1% solution of p-dimethylamino-phenylazoarsonic acid in ethanol containing 5% concentrated hydrochloric acid and rinse in $2N$ hydrochloric acid to remove the excess reagent. A brown line indicates zirconium.[25, 61]

Uranium

(58) Spray the sector with an approximately $1M$ solution of potassium ferrocyanide. A dark brown ring zone indicates uranium.[62, 63]

Barium

(59) Treat the sector with $1M$ sodium carbonate solution in order to fix the barium and then bathe in a freshly prepared saturated solution of sodium rhodizonate containing about 1% acetic acid. A red ring zone appears.[25, 64]

Strontium

(60) Test with sodium rhodizonate as described for barium.[25, 64]

Calcium

(61) Treat the ring zone by means of the hair-tipped capillary (as described in the tin test, p. 38) with a saturated aqueous solution of the osazone of dihydroxy-tartaric acid and remove the excess of reagent by rinsing with distilled water. A white-yellowish line indicates calcium ; its faint colour is readily visible when observed against the light. In cases where a white or very light yellow compound is formed as a result of an identification reaction, it is advisable to use commercially available black filter paper instead of the usual white paper ; the white colour can be seen much better.[25, 65]

(62) Treat the sector with an alizarin S-zirconium fluoride solution. (To 0.1% alizarin S solution add a few drops of a very dilute zirconium solution, then add 1% sodium fluoride solution dropwise until the solution turns yellow again.) The calcium precipitates the fluoride and demasks the zirconium, which reacts with the alizarin to form the violet zirconium-alizarin lake.[66]

Magnesium

(63) Spray the sector with a 0.01% solution of p-nitrobenzeneazo-resorcinol in $2N$ sodium hydroxide and wash well in distilled water. A blue line indicates magnesium.[25, 67]

(64) Test with quinalizarin as described for beryllium (test 54, p. 53).[58,68]

Sodium

(65) Spray the sector with, or dip it into, a solution of magnesium or zinc uranyl acetate and, while still moist, examine under U. V. light. A bright green fluorescent line indicates sodium.[25, 69]

Potassium

(66) Dip the sector into a saturated solution of sodium tetraphenyl-boron in water and rinse gently in distilled water. The white ring can be seen best in transmitted light. Here again, the use of black filter paper is preferable (cf. test 61 for calcium).[58, 70]

(67) Immerse the sector in a 1% aqueous solution of sodium dipicryl-amine (hexanitrodiphenylamine), rinse well under the tap, bathe in $0.1N$ nitric acid, and rinse again. A red line indicates potassium.[25, 71]

These tests for metal ions are summarized in Table 5. The last five columns give some idea of the concentration ranges in which the various tests can be used. Two factors normally determine the sensitivity of a spot reaction : the identification limit and the limiting concentration or dilution limit below which the reaction fails. Because the ring oven permits the concentration of very dilute solutions which would themselves fail to give a positive test in a particular reaction, the dilution limit of a test is not significant. The only significant factor is the actual amount collected in the ring. Thus it would be advantageous to use the ring oven technique for defining the identification limit, because comparisons can be made with different tests under exactly the same conditions.

In Table 5 the figures in the last five columns are the number of micrograms of the ion in the whole ring ; but only sectors of the whole rings are used, hence the actual amount in one test is only a fraction, a tenth or a twentieth, of the listed figure. The figures given are not intended as identification limits, but simply show whether or not a test gives a positive reaction at a certain concentration.

The standard solutions used in obtaining these figures were 0.1%, 0.05%, 0.01%, 0.005% and 0.001% with respect to the various metal ions. The drop size being 1.5 μl, the total amounts of metal in the rings are then 1.5, 0.75, 0.15, 0.075, and 0.015 μg. In reaction 15 for copper with dithio-oxamide, a ring prepared from 0.015 μg of copper is listed as giving a positive test ; but this does not mean that rings containing less copper would provide negative tests, i.e., 0.015 μg is not the identification limit. This extremely sensitive reaction would certainly still give positive tests with smaller amounts of copper.

The figures given cover only concentrations of 1 mg/ml to 0.01 mg/ml, for these are the concentrations which are most likely to occur in practice.

E. Reactions for Acid Radicals

It has become conventional to test for many ions which are in fact anions during the course of cation analysis. Familiar examples are aluminate, plumbite, stannite, molybdate and there are many more. Usually these ions are ignored in the anion scheme, because they are readily detected during cation analysis. However, many metal-containing ions are still tested for during anion analysis ; chromate, ferro- and ferricyanide are well-known examples of such ions.

The acid radicals are generally tested for in a specially prepared solution, from which most of the cations have been removed. Such anion solutions are prepared by treating the solution with sodium carbonate or by fusing the solid sample with sodium carbonate and then extracting with water.

No scheme has so far been worked out for a systematic separation of anions by means of the ring-oven, but there is little doubt that it could be effective. Although a systematic scheme has not yet been developed for the separation of anions in a single drop, a number of individual tests has been suggested and some of these are described below.[92]

The various points which were raised earlier in considering cation analysis (p. 47) also apply to anionic tests.

For more explicit details about the tests, Feigl's *Sp.t tests* should be consulted.

Bromide

(1) Spray the sector with a mixture of acetic acid and 3% hydrogen peroxide (1 : 5), dry, spray with a 0.5% solution of fluorescein in ethanol

Table 5. REACTIONS FOR METAL IONS

No.	Element	Reagent	Colour of ring	1.5	0.75	0.15	0.075	0.015
				μg in total ring				
1	Ag	p-Dimethylamino-benzylidene-rhodanine	red-violet	+	+	+	+	+
2	Ag	Chromate	red-brown	+	+	—	—	—
3	Ag	$Mn(II) + OH^-$	black	+	+	—	—	—
4	Ag	H_2S in acetone	black	+	+	+	+	+
5	Ag	$SnCl_2$	black	+	+	—	—	—
6	Hg	Diphenylcarbazide	violet-blue	+	+	+	+	—
7	Hg	$SnCl_2 +$ Aniline	black	+	+	—	—	—
8	Hg	Dithizone	orange	+	+	+	—	—
9	Hg	p-Dimethylamino-benzylidene-rhodanine	violet	+	+	—	—	—
10	Pb	Sodium rhodizonate	blue-violet-red	+	+	+	+	—
11	Pb	Benzidine	blue	+	+	—	—	—
12	Bi	Cinchonine + KI	orange	+	+	+	+	—
13	Bi	Alkaline stannite + $PbCl_2$	black	+	+	+	+	+
14	Bi	Alkaline stannite alone	black	+	+	+	—	—
15	Cu	Dithio-oxamide	olive green-black	+	+	+	+	+
16	Cu	Benzoinoxime	yellow-green	+	+	+	+	—
17	Cu	o-Tolidine + NH_4CNS	blue	+	+	+	+	—
18	Cu	H_2S in acetone + $AgNO_3$	black	+	+	+	+	—
19	Cu	2,2'-Diquinolyl (Cuproin)	violet red	+	+	+	+	—
20	Cu	$Fe^{3+} + CNS^- + S_2O_3^{2-}$	—	+	+	+	+	+
21	Cd	Ferrous dipyridiliodide	red	+	+	+	+	—
22	Cd	Cadion	pink	+	+	+	+	±
23	Cd	H_2S in acetone + $AgNO_3$	black	+	+	+	+	—

No.	Element	Reagent	Colour of ring	µg in total ring				
				1.5	0.75	0.15	0.075	0.015
24	As	Gutzeit test	yellow ; black					
25	Sb	Rhodamine B	blue	+	+	+	−	−
26	Sn	Morin	green fluorescence	+	+	+	+	−
27	Mo	$SnCl_2$ + KCNS	brick-red	+	+	+	+	−
28	Mo	Phenylhydrazine + acetic acid	red	+	+	+	−	−
29	W	$SnCl_2$	blue	+	+	−	−	−
30	W	Rhodamine B	violet	+	+	+	−	−
31	V	Aniline + HCl	dark blue	+	+	+	−	−
32	V	H_2O_2 + H_2SO_4	red-yellow	+	−	−	−	−
33	Au	Benzidine	blue	+	+	+	+	−
34	Au	p-Dimethylaminobenzyliden-rhodanine	violet	+	+	+	−	−
35	Pt	$SnCl_2$	orange	+	+	+	+	−
36	Co	a-nitroso-β-naphthol	red-brown	+	+	+	+	+
37	Co	Dithio-oxamide	brown	+	+	+	+	+
38	Co	NH_4CNS + acetone	blue	+	+	+	−	−
39	Ni	Dimethylglyoxime	red	+	+	+	+	−
40	Ni	Dithio-oxamide	violet	+	+	+	+	+
41	Fe	Potassium ferrocyanide	blue	+	+	+	+	+
42	Fe	KCNS	red	+	+	+	−	−
43	Fe	aa'-Dipyridyl + thioglycolic acid	red	+	+	+	+	±
44	Fe	Ferron	green	+	+	+	−	−
45	Cr	Diphenylcarbazide	violet	+	+	+	−	−

No.	Ele-ment	Reagent	Colour of ring	μg in total ring				
				1.5	0.75	0.15	0.075	0.015
46	Mn	3 : 3'-Dimethylnaphthidine	purple-red	+	+	+	+	—
47	Mn	Benzidine	blue	+	+	+	+	—
48	Mn	Silver Ammine Salt	black	+	+	+	+	—
49	Zn	$K_3[Fe(CN)_6]$ + 3 : 3'-di-methylnaphtidine	purple-red	+	+	+	+	—
50	Zn	$[Hg(CNS)_4]^{2-}$ + Co^{2+}	blue	+	+	+	+	—
51	Al	Morin	yellow-green fluorescence	+	+	+	+	+
52	Al	Aluminon	dark-red	+	+	+	+	—
53	Al	Alizarin S	red	+	+	+	—	—
54	Be	Quinalizarin	red	+	+	+	+	±
55	Be	Morin + NH_4OH	green fluorescence	+	+	+	+	+
56	Ti	Chromotropic acid	brown-red	+	+	+	—	—
57	Zr	p-Dimethylaminoazophenyl-arsonic acid	brown	+	+	+	+	—
58	U	Potassium ferrocyanide	brown	5μg	—	—	—	—
59	Ba	Sodium rhodizonate	red	+	+	+	—	—
60	Sr	Sodium rhodizonate	red	+	+	—	—	—
61	Ca	Dihydroxytartaric acid osazone	yellow	+	+	+	—	—
62	Ca	Zirconium-fluoride-alizarin	red-violet	+	+	+	—	—
63	Mg	p-Nitrobenzeneresorcinol	blue	+	+	+	+	—
64	Mg	Quinalizarin	blue	+	+	+	—	—
65	Na	Magnesium uranyl acetate	in U.V. green fluorescence	+	+	—	—	—
66	K	Sodium tetraphenylboron	white	+	+	—	—	—
67	K	Dipicrylamine	red	+	+	—	—	—

and again dry. A red line of tetrabromofluorescein (eosin) indicates bromide.[72, 73]

Iodide

(2) Spray the sector with a 1% aqueous palladous chloride solution. A brown-black line of palladous iodide appears.[74]

(3) Fume the sector over hydrochloric acid and spray with a 1% aqueous solution of thallous nitrate. A yellow line of thallous iodide indicates iodide.[75]

Fluoride

(4) Test with aluminium chromazurol S.[76] See page 64.

Thiocyanate

(5) Fume the filter paper over hydrochloric acid and spray with a 1% iron(III) chloride solution. A red line denotes thiocyanate.

(6) Spray the sector with a copper sulphate solution, which contains a few drops of dilute sulphuric acid and has been reduced with sodium bisulphite. Wash the copper(I) thiocyanate thoroughly under the tap, fume over ammonium sulphide, again wash well with water and finally bathe in a 1% silver nitrate solution. A black line of silver sulphide denotes thiocyanate.

Ferrocyanide

(7) Spray the sector with a 1N uranyl acetate solution. A brown line indicates ferrocyanide.[77]

(8) Develop the line by spraying with a 0.1N iron(III) chloride solution. A blue colour denotes ferrocyanide. It is advisable to treat the ring zone first with a zinc solution in order to fix the ferrocyanide, to rinse well and then to spray with iron(III) chloride solution.

Ferricyanide

(9) Spray the paper with a 0.1N iron(II) chloride solution. A blue line appears (Turnbull's blue).

(10) Spray the sector first with a 1% zinc sulphate solution and then with acetic acid—benzidine solution. A blue line indicates ferricyanide.[78, 79]

Bromate

(11) Reduce the bromate to bromide by holding the paper in a sulphur dioxide atmosphere from sodium bisulphite and sulphuric acid.

The gas generator (p. 21) may be used if desired. Then detect the bromide formed with fluorescein solution as described in reaction 1 (p. 56).

Iodate

(12) Spray a freshly prepared mixture of potassium iodide solution, starch solution and acetic acid on to the sector. A blue line indicates iodate, provided that other oxidizing substances are absent.

(13) Spray the sector with a solution of pyrogallol and oxalic acid in acetone. A yellow to red ring indicates iodate.[80]

Sulphide

(14) Spray the sector with a 1% silver nitrate solution. A brown-black line of silver sulphide appears.

Sulphite

(15) Spray the sector with lead nitrate solution, rinse well under the tap and fume over ammonium sulphide solution. A brown line of lead sulphide appears.

Sulphate

(16) Spray the paper with lead nitrate solution, rinse well under the tap and develop the lead with a sodium rhodizonate solution (see reaction 10, p. 49).

(17) Apply reaction 15 as for sulphite.

Nitrate

(18) Place the sector on a zinc plate, spray with an acetic acid mixture of sulphanilic acid and a-naphthylamine solution and press against the zinc plate. The nitrate is thus reduced without the sharp line becoming blurred and the nitrite in the ring reacts with the reagent mixture to form a red azo dye.[81]

Nitrite

(19) Spray the sector with a $0.1N$ potassium iodide solution containing starch, dry and then spray with dilute acetic acid. A blue line indicates nitrite. Other oxidizing agents must be absent.

(20) Spray the sector with an acetic acid solution of sulphanilic acid and a-naphthylamine. A red line indicates nitrite (cf. reaction 18).[81, 82]

Phosphate

(21) Spray the paper quickly with a 4% nitric acid solution of ammonium molybdate and dry; repeat three times. Finally, spray with an acetic acid solution of benzidine and neutralize by fuming over ammonia solution. A blue line appears if phosphate is present.[83]

Borate

(22) Fume the sector over hydrochloric acid, spray with a saturated alcoholic solution of turmeric (curcuma) and dry. A red line appears, which turns blue on spotting with a 1% sodium hydroxide solution.[84]

Chromate

(23) Spray the sector with a 1% alcoholic solution of diphenylcarbazide and fume over concentrated hydrochloric acid. A violet line indicates chromate. Compare p. 40 and p. 58.

The tests for acid radicals are summarized in Table 6.

F. Practical Applications of the Qualitative Ring Oven Method

The various methods for qualitative analysis so far described have found many practical applications which are discussed on the following pages. Three specialized qualitative applications are first discussed, i. e. the identification of fluoride, the separation and identification of tungsten and molybdenum, and the separation of uranium from thorium, bismuth and lead, because these three examples demonstrate the use of the ring oven to solve specific problems. Some practical applications in industrial routine analysis and chemical research are also cited.

(1) Identification of fluoride ion[76]

This application is an example of a qualitative test which is possible only on the microscale with the ring oven. An old and frequently used method of detecting or determining fluoride is by a bleaching reaction ; a metal-dyestuff complex (the metal is usually aluminium, zirconium, or thorium) is treated with the

Table 6. REACTIONS FOR ANIONS

Nr.	Ion	Reagent	Colour	μg in total ring				
				1.5	0.75	0.15	0.075	0.015
1	Br^-	Fluorescein	red	+	+	—	—	—
2	I^-	Palladous chloride	brown-black	+	+	+	—	—
3	I^-	Thallous nitrate	yellow	+	+	—	—	—
4	F^-	Al-chromazurol S—Al	blue	+	+	+	+	+
5	CNS^-	$FeCl_3$	red	+	+	+	—	—
6	CNS^-	$Cu(I) + H_2S + AgNO_3$	black	+	+	±	—	—
7	$[Fe(CN)_6]^{4-}$	$(UO_2)(CH_3COO)_2$	red brown	+	+	—	—	—
8	$[Fe(CN)_6]^{4-}$	$FeCl_3$	blue	+	+	—	—	—
9	$[Fe(CN)_6]^{3-}$	$FeCl_2$	blue	+	+	—	—	—
10	$[Fe(CN)_6]^{3-}$	Benzidine $+ ZnSO_4$	blue	+	+	—	—	—
11	BrO_3^-	$NaHSO_3$, Fluorescein	red	+	+	—	—	—
12	IO_3^-	KI + starch	blue	+	+	+	+	—
13	IO_3^-	Pyrogallol	yellow-red	+	+	+	—	—
14	S^{2-}	$AgNO_3$	brown-black	+	+	+	+	—
15	SO_3^{2-}	$Pb(NO_3)_2 + S^{2-}$	brown	+	+	+	—	—
16	SO_4^{2-}	$Pb(NO_3)_2 +$ Sodium rhodizonate	violet-blue	+	+	+	—	—
17	SO_4^{2-}	$Pb(NO_3)_2 + S^{2-}$	brown	+	+	+	—	—
18	NO_3^-	Sulphanilic acid $+ a$-naphthylamine on Zn-plate	red	+	+	+	—	—
19	NO_2^-	KI + starch	blue	+	+	+	—	—
20	NO_2^-	Sulphanilic acid $+ a$-naphthylamine	red	+	+	+	—	—
21	PO_4^{3-}	$(NH_4)_2MoO_4 +$ Benzidine	blue	+	+	+	+	—
22	BO_3^{3-}	Turmeric, NaOH	red-blue	+	+	+	+	+
23	CrO_4^{2-}	Diphenylcarbazide	violet	+	+	+	±	—

sample, the metal fluoride is formed and bleaching results from the destruction of the highly coloured complex. The colour becomes *less* intense as the amount of fluoride ion increases. Obviousiy, it would be preferable for the colour intensity to increase with increasing amounts of fluoride and this can be achieved by means of the ring oven.

Procedure: Place a drop of the blue solution of complex aluminium—chromazurol S[85] in the centre of a filter paper and dry at 60—70° C. The reagent solution must be free from excess of aluminium or of the triphenylmethane dyestuff, chromazurol S. This can be achieved by adding an excess of dyestuff solution and removing the excess by extraction with ether. The pH of the solution should be kept at about 4.3, by means of an ammonium acetate—acetic acid buffer.

Fume a drop of the sample solution in the capillary sample pipette over acetic acid, spot it on to the blue reagent spot and dry at 60—70° C. The fluoride releases part of the red chromazurol S, which cannot be seen on the dark blue spot. Place the filter on the ring oven and extract the released red chromazurol S with ethanol, thus forming a red ring zone, whereas the blue aluminium-chromazurol S remains in the centre spot. The outer ring can be more easily observed by spraying with an aluminium chloride solution which forms a clear blue ring of aluminium-chromazurol S.

The more fluoride present, the more intense is the colour of the rings. The sensitivity of this test is 0.005 μg of fluoride.

(2) Separation of micro-amounts of molybdenum and tungsten[43]

A number of methods for detecting tungsten and molybdenum have been reported in the literature, but their separation and identification are still difficult when only micro-amounts of sample are available, especially when the proportion of one metal is high. A simple and very sensitive separation of tungsten and molybdenum has been worked out by the ring oven method.

Procedure: Place a drop of the aqueous solution containing about 1.5 μg of the metals in the centre of a round filter, ring it and then spot with a 30% aqueous solution of quinine hydrochloride ; this treatment fixes the tungsten in the spot. Place the paper on the ring oven and wash all the molybdenum into the ring zone with 0.1N hydrochloric acid. Dry the paper, punch out the inner spot containing the tungsten, place it on another filter and again extract on the ring oven with 0.1N ammonia solution. Spray a sector of the first ring with a 10% solution of thiocyanate and a 5% solution of stannous chloride in 3N hydrochloric acid, which forms a brick-red line with molybdenum. Develop a sector of the second ring by immersion in a 0.1% rhodamine B solution in 6N hydrochloric acid and rinse carefully under the tap. A violet ring indicates tungsten. The tungsten need not be fixed quantitatively in the middle, but all the molybdenum must be completely removed from the centre spot.

Separation and identification can be performed in mixtures over the range containing 1—100 µg of tungsten and 1—5 µg of molybdenum.

(3) Separation of uranium from thorium, bismuth and lead[62]

The present importance of uranium has greatly increased the demand for new methods for its identification, separation and determination. Separation and identification on the microscale are particularly necessary in nuclear investigations. Uranium samples often contain thorium, lead and bismuth (^{212}Pb, ^{212}Bi) owing to decay reactions.

Several physicochemical methods are available for the separation and identification of uranium, such as paper chromatography, particle counting or extraction. The ring oven technique provides a purely chemical method for separating microgram amounts of uranium from large quantities of thorium, lead and bismuth. It is also possible to determine the uranium semiquantitatively (Chapter III, p. 78).

Procedure: Place a drop of the sample solution in the centre of a filter paper and treat with hydrogen fluoride (generated in the usual manner from a fluoride and sulphuric acid in a lead crucible) to precipitate the thorium. Fume over ammonia solution to ensure complete precipitation. Fix lead and bismuth as sulphides in the same spot, using the gas generator (p. 21).

Place the paper on the ring oven and wash all the uranium out with 0.1N hydrochloric acid. Spray a sector of this ring with a 1M solution of potassium ferrocyanide. A brown line indicates uranium.

The method gives good results even when the amounts of the three accompanying metals present are 100 times that of uranium.

(4) Some other applications

As generally happens in microanalytical work, the ring oven method was first used only when the amount of sample available was extremely small. But the simplicity and rapidity of the technique encouraged its adoption even when there was no lack of test substance. Applications of this type are now at least as numerous as those where a micromethod is the only possibility.

Qualitative analysis by the ring oven method has been used in art investigations, where no visible attack on valuable *objets d'art* can be tolerated and only a few micrograms of the sample can be taken by a special method. The composition of coins and of ancient Egyptian bronzes[86] has been determined in this way.

The ring oven method has been also applied in investigating the paints in old paintings, where only trace samples are permissible. However, the method has also been used for systematic analyses of pigments in the modern paint industry.

The technique has been used in checking the corrosion of different metals by the analysis of the corrosion products, for only very small amounts of these are sometimes available.

The inorganic components of rubber, textiles, oils and foodstuffs[87] have been identified in this way after ashing the organic material and extracting the ash with acid. The ring oven has also proved its value in the coal industry for the analysis of metals in coal ash, and in several metal industries for the rapid investigation of alloy compositions. It has assisted in the solution of several special problems in the electronics field (Mo—W).

The "one drop method" has also found frequent application in solving criminological problems.

The application of the ring oven method in trace analysis has been discussed,[88] and its use in air pollution investigations has been suggested.[89]

These few examples which cover a wide range of industrial and scientific research, indicate the greatly varied possibilities of this technique.

G. REAGENTS AND FILTER PAPER

As in any microanalytical work, the purity of the reagents is extremely important in the ring oven method. This is especially true for the reagent solutions used for elution on the ring oven, because any impurities in the wash liquid accumulate in the ring zone and might then interfere with the identification reactions.

However, acids, such as hydrochloric acid are used only as dilute (0.05 or 0.1N) solutions in the washing procedures, so that the contaminants in analytical grade reagents should do no harm, provided that the water used for diluting contains no impurities itself. The water should be distilled in a glass distillation apparatus, and in very delicate investigations, double distilled water is preferable.

In order to check the quality of the reagents, blank tests should be carried out regularly.

Organic solvents of high grade purity should be used and these should be freshly distilled if necessary.

Reagents such as hydrochloric acid, acetic acid or ammonia solution are readily purified by isothermal distillation.[90] A glass vessel containing the reagent solution to be purified is placed in an empty desiccator containing a second glass dish filled with double distilled water. After the system has stood overnight, the water contains enough of the reagent to be used as extractant on the ring oven.

The filter paper offers more serious problems because all the impurities in the inner circle of 22 mm (the diameter of the borehole) are extracted from the paper and concentrated in the ring zone. Therefore only quantitative grade filter papers such as Schleicher-Schüll 589[2] or Whatman 40 can be used.

Papers can be rapidly and easily tested for their impurities by means of the ring oven in order to discover which is best suited for a particular purpose. The method is of interest not only for the present purpose, but also in techniques such as spot analysis, paper chromatography and paper electrophoresis.

In this method of determining impurities,[91] soluble materials are washed out of a circular area of the paper and concentrated in a sharp ring zone. The concentrations of the impurities are effected as follows. The impurities are extracted from a circle of diameter 22 mm, which thus has an area of approximately 380 mm^2; and they are finally concentrated in a ring of width 0.1mm and circumference 70 mm whose area is about 7 mm^2. The concentration factor is therefore 380 : 7 = 54. The concentration of the impurities in the ring is at least 54 times greater than that in the paper itself, thus many substances which would otherwise escape identification can be detected.

For example, if 0.1N hydrochloric acid is used to extract the paper on the ring oven, heavy metals are concentrated in the ring zone. The dried paper is cut in half, and iron, one of the commonest contaminants, is tested for with potassium ferrocyanide. Heavy metals in general are revealed on the other half by treatment with ammonium sulphide solution and conversion of the metal sulphides to silver sulphide. Specific reagents can be applied to detect any particular substance which may be present.

Chloride, another very common contaminant, can be concentrated in a ring zone by extracting the paper on the ring oven with twice distilled water. The paper is dried and bathed in a 1% silver nitrate solution, which fixes the chloride as well as other ions that form sparingly soluble silver compounds. After the excess of silver nitrate has been removed, the chloride ring is developed by treatment with ammonium sulphide solution.

Apart from these two examples, selective extraction can be achieved by the right choice of solvent.

When this is done with a number of different papers, the intensities of the rings can be compared and the paper which is best suited for a particular purpose can easily be selected. Impurities in filter papers can often be detected without concentration by means of very sensitive reactions.[93]

Other filter materials, such as glass fibre filters or plastic filters (PVC) would be very useful in working with sulphuric acid which destroys ordinary filter paper. Unfortunately, neither of these materials are at present satisfactory enough to be recommended. When this problem is solved, still more flexibility and further extensions in the application of the ring oven method are to be expected.

CHAPTER III

SEMI QUANTITATIVE ANALYSIS

A. SPOT COLORIMETRY

A REVIEW of the current literature dealing with analytical chemistry shows an increasing interest in semi-quantitative analytical methods. Many of the methods do not use the term "semi-quantitative" in the title, but in fact their accuracy is well outside the normal acceptable limits in quantitative analysis. There is no definite border line between semi-quantitative and quantitative methods; semi-quantitative methods could be defined as analytical techniques which provide results with comparatively higher degrees of error; the limits of these errors must, of course, be known.

There are three occasions for using semi-quantitative methods :

1. In cases where better methods are not available, e. g. because of the small size of the sample ;
2. As a preliminary method of obtaining rapid information before applying more elaborate analysis ;
3. In cases where no more precise results are needed, e. g. to find out the type of an alloy.

Semi-quantitative analytical procedures are usually very simple, rapid and economical; advantages which are at present quite essential in many industrial laboratories.

The sensitivity and, in many cases, the specificity of spot reactions long ago suggested their use in semi-quantitative analysis. The comparison of the colour intensity of a spot with that of a standard scale allows the concentration of the unknown solution to be estimated, and, if the volume is known, the amount of the substance can be determined.

The reactions can be carried out on a spot plate or on filter paper ; in the latter case, the standard scale can often be preserved which offers some convenience. Tananaeff in 1928 coined the name "spot colorimetry" for this type of analysis. Feigl in his *Laboratory Manual of Spot Tests* (Academic Press, New York, 1943) gives a survey of problems, methods and results involving this technique.

In 1937, Yagoda[94] developed the method with the so-called "confined spot test paper", a filter paper which is impregnated with waxes or similar products apart from small round areas of definite size, on which the drop of sample solution is placed ; this results in a more homogeneous colour after developing with a suitable reagent.

Nevertheless, the comparison of colours in spot colorimetry involves many errors. It is difficult to make a precise colour estimate in order to align the spot with the standard scale. Owing to adsorption reactions, the spots are frequently inhomogeneous, which also leads to excessive errors.

The ring oven allows the collection of substances in the form of sharp well-defined rings, which can be regarded as "circular spots", and which are independent of the number of drops from which they have been made ; it is thus possible to apply the method to spot colorimetry. For this type of analysis, Stephen[58] has suggested the term "ring colorimetry".

B. Spot Colorimetry with the Ring Oven Method[95, 96] Ring Colorimetry

The difficulty of precise alignment of a sample spot in a standard scale can be circumvented by preparing several "circular spots", or rings (instead of only one) from varying numbers of sample drops, developing the rings with a suitable reagent and comparing with a standard scale. The errors are thus remarkably reduced by compensation of error, although only a rough alignment to the standard scale is necessary. The arrangement acts somewhat like a "chemical vernier" (nonius), and is only possible by the use of the ring oven. The colour intensity or diameter of a certain ring is obviously independent of the number of drops used to form the ring ; the colour intensity is determined solely by the total amount of substance in the particular ring zone.

The colour intensities of the various sample and standard rings are compared by direct observation ; the rings should be observed in both transmitted and direct light.

Only one standard solution is necessary for preparing the standard scale because the standard rings differ only in the number of standard solution drops from which they are made. The volume of the drops need not be known, provided that they are always the same size ; this is readily achieved by means of the self-filling sampling pipette (p. 22). It is convenient to use a sample pipette with a volume of about 1.5 μl, as used for the qualitative work. This pipette should be carefully stored, for its loss would mean the preparation of new standard scales. The filter paper used in the preparation of a particular standard scale must be the same as that used in the determination ; only quantitative grade filter paper should be employed.

In spot colorimetry, as in any kind of colorimetry, observable differences in colour intensity occur only within a certain range of concentration. The concentrations of standard solution required depend on the reaction used and on the drop size. If the reaction has a higher sensitivity, a more dilute standard solution must be chosen and vice versa. Because the concentration of the substance in the ring depends on the drop size, and because this size is kept constant by using the same capillary pipette, the concentration of the standard solution depends only on the reaction used.

In working out the method for a given ion, one must use a reaction which produces a coloured insoluble product. If this product is stable for a long period of time, the standard scale can be preserved, which is an obvious advantage.

The range of concentrations over which observable differences in colour intensity can be obtained must then be determined. The optimal concentration will always be in the region where drop furnishes a just visible reaction, i. e., near the identi-
ation limit.

The following desription of the determination of iron and the preparation of an iron standard scale illustrates the application of a semi-quantitative determination with the ring oven.

(1) The determination of iron

For the semi-quantitative determination of iron, the reaction with potassium ferrocyanide is used. The drop size is about 1.5 μl. A standard solution of iron(III) chloride which contains 0.1 mg of iron/ml is used.

Preparation of standard scale: Place one drop of this solution in the centre of a filter paper and wash on the ring oven into the ring zone with 0.05N hydrochloric acid. It is necessary to elute from the exact centre of the spot in order to distribute the iron from the spot equally into the ring ; this is easily done by marking the centre of the paper with a needle and placing the tip of the sample capillary pipette on this point. If the washing capillary is also put exactly on this point, equal distribution of the iron into the ring is obtained. This marking technique must also be used in the preparation of a standard ring when several drops are added.

When the iron has been collected in the ring zone, dry the filter and fume first over hydrochloric acid and then over bromine water for oxidation. Bathe in a 1% aqueous solution of potassium ferrocyanide and rinse thoroughly under the tap. A uniform blue ring is obtained. Place the paper between sheets of blotting paper to remove excess of moisture and then dry without warming. In this particular case, drying in an oven may affect the colour. This ring becomes number I of the standard scale.

Prepare rings with 2, 4, 6, 8 and 10 drops of standard solution in the same way, and number them II, IV, VI, VIII and X. About 30 minutes are required for the preparation of this scale. When more than 4 drops are used, dry the paper between drop additions to prevent the formation of too large spots.

It is fruitless to prepare additional standard rings with a higher number of drops because the differences in colour intensity are insufficiently distinct ; 6 standard rings suffice.

This scale is stable for a long time and can be used repeatedly provided that the same conditions of dropsize, reagents and filter paper are maintained. The colour intensities of these six standard rings are sufficiently distinct for differences to be easily recognized.

Determination of iron: Place one drop of the unknown solution on the filter paper, wash into the ring zone and develop with potassium ferr cyanide as described for the preparation of the standard scale. The unknown and standard rings must be treated identically. Wash the ring thoroughly, dry it in air and compare with the standard scale. It is unnecessary to make a precise estimate at this stage.

For example, the unknown ring 1 (from one drop of the unknown solution) may match between the standard rings number I and II. Then two more "unknown" rings are prepared with sufficient test drops to cover as large a range as possible of the whole scale. In this particular example, ring 1 fits between standard rings I and II, hence two more rings are prepared from two and three drops of the unknown solution. The three unknown rings are finally compared with the standard scale. This should be done in two steps.

In the "first guess" the unknown rings need only be matched roughly with the standard scale. Assume that the three unknown rings match respectively between standard ring I and II, II and IV, and VI and VIII. A more precise comparison, or "second guess", can then be made. Only three possibilities are available for this decision : a particular ring is more closely matched with either one or other of the two standard rings between which it has been placed in the "first guess", or no decision can be made in which case the number in between must be recorded.

In the above example, the following numbers would have been found :

Unknown rings	Standard rings "first guess"	"second guess"
1 drop	I— II	2
2 drops	II— IV	4
3 drops	VI—VIII	8
6 drops		14

The numbers of drops contained in the three unknown rings are then added ($1 + 2 + 3 = \underline{6}$), and the corresponding standard ring numbers, i. e. the numbers of standard solution drops, are also added ($2 + 4 + 8 = \underline{14}$). These two totals mean that a ring made of 6 unknown drops would correspond theoretically to a ring of 14 drops of standard solution ; such rings are, of course, useless in practice because the difference in colour intensity in this range could not be seen. The figure obtained by the division $14/6 = 2.33$ is the concentration of the unknown solution referred to the standard solution. When this number is multiplied by the concentration of the standard solution (0.1 mg/ml) the concentration of the unknown sample solution (0.233 mg of iron/ml) is obtained.

(The actual concentration of iron in this example was 0.230 mg/ml; the error is less than 2%.) The concentration and the volume of the sample solution are now known and the percentage of iron in the sample can be calculated.

The error in most cases is of the order of $\pm$ 5—10%, but is often less. This seems to be satisfactory considering that no optical apparatus is used and that the sample for the analysis is extremely small.

A short calculation will give some idea of the amount of sample involved. The volume of the 6 drops used to produce the three unknown rings was 9 μl. The sample solution was found to contain 0.233 mg of iron/ml, hence the total amount of iron in the three rings was 2.1 μg. The sample used is always of this order of magnitude, for a higher drop number must be connected with a lower concentration.

The colour intensities are best compared on a pearl glass screen illuminated from below. In some cases, it may be advisable to treat the paper with liquid paraffin, which makes the paper translucent and thus the colours more visible. The colours can also be compared by projecting the standard scale and the test rings on to a screen by means of an epidiascope.

Such a semi-quantitative determination takes only about 1—020 minutes if a standard scale is available.

In general, when a ring is made from one drop of the unknown solution and compared with the standard scale, there are three possibilities :

1. The ring is less intense than standard ring I ; hence the unknown solution is weaker than the standard solution and rings must be made with larger numbers of drops, say 5, 7 and 10 or even more.
2. The ring is more intense than standard ring X. The unknown solution must therefore be more than ten times stronger than the standard solution and must be diluted to fall within the standard scale before the three rings are made.
3. The ring fits into the standard scale, as in the example described above, the concentration of the unknown lying between that of the standard solution and ten times as much. This generally happens in practice, because the percentage of a substance in the sample is usually known approximately and the range of concentration can be chosen by a suitable dilution.

It is always necessary to prepare three different rings of the unknown solution, and the three rings must cover as wide a range of the scale as possible in order to obtain the optimum results.

If the unknown ring 1 (consisting of 1 drop) corresponds to standard rings I—II, then two extra rings are made with 2 and 3 drops, 2 and 4 drops or even 3 and 5 drops. If the first ring corresponds more closely to standard ring IV, the next ring can be made with 2 drops, but a ring with 3 drops would fall outside the scale range. To avoid tedious dilution of the sample solution, the third ring can be made with half a drop. The following procedure is used to circumvent the problems of measuring this minute volume correctly in relation to the capillary sample pipette. One drop of the unknown solution is placed on two filter papers lying together, and the drop is washed into the ring zone of both filters on the hot ring oven in the usual way. Each of the ring zones on the two filters then contains virtually half of the original sample drop. Rings from 1.5 drops can be similarly prepared by placing three drops on to two filter papers.

The following example of an analysis of an iron solution containing 0.46 mg of iron/ml uses rings with $\frac{1}{2}$ and $1\frac{1}{2}$ drops :

| Unknown rings | Standard rings | |
	"first guess"	"second guess"
$\frac{1}{2}$ drop	II— IV	3
1 drop	IV— VI	5
$1\frac{1}{2}$ drops	VI—VIII	7
3 drops		15
$15 : 3 = 5$	$0.1 \times 5 = 0.5$ mg Fe/ml	

The fact that the results are fairly precise (about $\pm$ 5—10% error or even less) is surprising, considering that only the nearest integer is guessed and that there is a limited number of possibilities for estimating the intensities of the rings in comparison with the standard scale, viz. 1, 1.5, 2, 3, 4, 5, 6, 7, 8, 9,10. A simple mathematical treatment explains this (97) :

Let the quotient

$$\frac{\text{concentration of the unknown solution}}{\text{concentration of the standard solution}} = a$$

Suppose that n rings, $R_1, R_2, R_3 \ldots R_n$, are washed from p_1, p_2, $p_3 \ldots p_n$ drops, and that the rings $R_1, R_2, R_3 \ldots R_n$ correspond to the standard rings $k_1, k_2, k_3 \ldots k_n$. Then each of the fractions k_1/p_1, $/p_2$, $k_3/p_3 \ldots k_n/p_n$ gives an approximate value for a.

As shown in the examples for the iron determination, the results are calculated as follows .

$$\beta = \frac{k_1 + k_2 + \cdots\cdots k_n}{p_1 + p_2 + \cdots\cdots p_n}$$

where β is the practical result for α.
This equation can be also written as

$$\beta = \frac{p_1 \times k_1/p_1 + p_2 \times k_2/p_2 + \cdots p_n \times k_n/p_n}{p_1 + p_2 + \cdots p_n}$$

which is simply the "weighted average" for the single results k_1/p_1, k_2/p_2, $k_3/p_3 \ldots k_n/p_n$. This average is much more likely to be near the correct result than any single estimate. In ideal cases, of course, $\beta = \alpha$.

It can be shown statistically that if three rings are used ($n = 3$), as in the above two examples, the expected accuracy is better than $\pm 5\%$; the more rings with different drop numbers, the better the result, but for semi-quantitative purposes three rings suffice.

(2) The determination of other metals

The semi-quantitative determination of ten metals by techniques similar to that for iron is described below. Similar methods for other metal ions as well as for acidic radicals could, of course, be developed. Unless stated otherwise, scales of standard rings are prepared from 1, 2, 4, 6, 8 and 10 drops of standard solution.

Nickel

The concentration of the nickel standard solution is 0.1 mg of nickel/ml, and the drop size is again about 1.5 μl.

Prepare a scale of standard rings. Dry these rings, fume over ammonia solution, spray with a 1% solution of dimethylglyoxime in ethanol and dry in a drying oven. Prepare sample rings under the same conditions and compare with the standard scale.

Cobalt

The concentration of the cobalt standard solution is 0.1 mg of cobalt/ml with a drop size of about 1.5 μl.

Dry the rings, spray with a 0.5% solution of α-nitroso-β-naphthol in acetone and again dry for a short time. The dry filters show red-brow rings of the cobalt-complex on a yellowish background ; this yellow coloration comes from the excess of α-nitroso-β-naphthol and would render the colour comparison more difficult. Therefore, wash the dried filters in an ammonia solution (1 : 5) and rinse under the tap to remove the excess of reagent. In the same way, prepare the unknown rings, develop, treat with ammonia solution and finally compare with the standard scale.

Copper

For the determination of copper its reaction with α-benzoinoxime can be used ; the reaction with dithio-oxamide (rubeanic acid) has also been applied, especially where only very low copper concentrations are available, for this reaction has a high sensitivity. The best procedure proved to be the following.

Bathe the rings containing the copper in a solution of hydrogen sulphide containing a few drops of hydrochloric acid. Then rinse the filters carefully, first under the tap and then with distilled water to remove excess hydrogen sulphide. Bathe the filters in a 1% solution of silver nitrate ; silver sulphide is thus precipitated in the ring in an amount equivalent to the copper sulphide. Rinse the papers quickly in distilled water, then under the tap and finally dry them.

The silver sulphide rings are stable for a long time and have a brown-black colour which is very convenient for estimating purposes. The washing with distilled water is necessary because of the chloride content of most tap water ; silver chloride would be formed in the paper, decompose and tint the paper greyish-brown. Washing with distilled water before and after the treatment with silver nitrate avoids this disadvantage.

The concentration of the copper standard solution is 0.1 mg of copper/ml. Prepare the standard rings as described. Develop the sample rings in the same way and compare with the standard scale.

Cadmium

Carry out the analysis exactly as described for copper.[58]

Aluminium

An aluminium chloride solution containing 0.1 mg of aluminium/ml is used as standard solution. Wash the standard rings on the ring oven with 0.1N hydrochloric acid. Dry the rings, wash in a 0.1% solution of alizarin S or quinalizarin in 2N ammonia solution, rinse well with water and treat with 1N acetic acid. After washing with water, dry the filters. Quinalizarin forms violet rings and alizarin S, red rings ; both are stable. Develop the unknown rings in the same way.[58]

Beryllium

The concentration of the beryllium standard solution is 0.1 mg of beryllium/ml. Develop the standard rings by immersing the papers in a solution of 0.05 g of quinalizarin in 100 ml of 0.1N sodium hydroxide. Wash under the tap, treat with 1N acetic acid and again wash. The rings are stable for a long time. Develop the sample rings in the same way.[58]

Magnesium

The magnesium standard solution contains 0.1 mg of magnesium/ml. Bathe the standard rings in a solution of 0.05 g of quinalizarin in 100 ml of 0.1N sodium hydroxide, wash thoroughly and dry. Blue stable standard rings are obtained.[58]

Potassium

The standard solution contains 0.3 mg of potassium/ml. Develop the standard rings by immersing in a 1% aqueous solution of sodium hexanitrodiphenylamine, rinse well and bathe in 0.1N nitric acid. Wash the papers carefully in water, and dry them. The standard scale is stable.

Potassium can also be determined by its reaction with sodium tetraphenylboron. This reaction gives white precipitates, which are difficult to compare; the use of black filter paper is advisable in this case.[58]

Zinc

The zinc chloride standard solution contains 0.1 mg of zinc/ml. Develop the rings in the following way. Apply a 1% aqueous solution of potassium ferricyanide only along the outline of the ring zone by means of a capillary (compare test for tin, p. 38). Treat the zinc ferricyanide thus formed in the rings with a saturated solution of 3 : 3-dimethylnaphthidine in 1N hydrochloric acid, which is also applied to the ring-zone by means of a capillary. Wash with distilled water to obtain sharp outlined purple rings of the oxidized reagent adsorbed on zinc ferrocyanide. The standard rings are stable only for several hours and must therefore be prepared always fresh. [55,58]

Uranium

For the semi-quantitative determination of uranium, a somewhat unusual procedure has been described by Antikainen. The differences are probably due to the low sensitivity of the reaction between uranium and ferrocyanide.

Prepare a standard scale consisting of eight standard rings, containing 10, 20, 40, 80, 120, 160, 200 and 240 μg of uranium. Use uranium nitrate in the standard solution, and measure the drop volumes with a micro-syringe pipette. Develop the standard rings by spraying with a $1M$ solution of potassium ferrocyanide. Prepare sample rings of the unknown solution in the same way from precisely measured volumes. (Compare the method for separating the uranium from thorium, lead and bismuth, p. 65).[62]

(3) Removal of interfering ions

The ion to be determined by means of spot colorimetry using the ring oven is in all practical cases, of course, not the only solute in the sample solution. The removal of interfering ions is obviously important. Interferences will arise from ions which,

  a. give a coloured precipitate with the reagent required,
  b. retard the reaction, or
  c. are themselves coloured (this can be overcome by final rinsing of the rings).

There is normally no need to separate these interfering ions before applying the test drop to the paper, because these difficulties can be overcome directly on the paper. There are two possible techniques.

  a. The interfering ion can be fixed in the centre. For example, when iron is determined with potassium ferrocyanide in the presence of copper, the copper can be precipitated in the original spot with hydrogen sulphide and the iron washed into the ring zone where it is developed with potassium ferrocyanide.

Another example is the determination of uranium in presence of thorium, lead and bismuth (pp. 65 and 68).

  b. The interfering substances can be removed from the developed ring. For example, when nickel is determined in a solution containing iron, both ions are washed into the ring zone with $0.1N$ hydrochloric acid. When the ring is fumed over ammonia solution before being sprayed with dimethylglyoxime solution, the iron precipitates as iron(III) hydroxide which interferes with the red colour of nickel dimethylglyoxime. The iron(III) hydroxide is therefore removed from the nickel dimethylglyoxime ring by final bathing in a tartrate solution. After drying the rings can be compared with the nickel standard scale.

There are, of course, alternative methods if ions present are expected to cause any difficulties. The correct use of analytical reactions such as precipitating in the centre, masking, and choice of selective reactions for developing the rings, nearly always permits the interference of accompanying ions to be overcome.

If an interfering ion is present in an extremely high concentration it may be advisable to remove it before applying the sample drops to the paper. This can easily be done by microanalytical methods, because the volume of test solution needs only be very small and the separations can be completed very quickly. Precipitation with gaseous reagents should be used whenever possible for the removal of interfering ions, no matter whether the precipitate or the remaining solution contains the ion to be determined.

C. The Universal Standard Scale[98]

The semi-quantitative method requires a standard scale for comparison, and in the method just described, scales must be prepared for each element to be determined. Although this is relatively easy and takes only about 30 minutes, it would be more convenient to have one standard scale with which several ions could be compared. At first glance this seems impracticable, because of the different colours of the sample rings derived from different elements. Nevertheless, the determinations of copper and cadmium by means of precipitation with hydrogen sulphide (p. 77) hint at such possibilities.

In the copper determination, the copper standard and sample rings are developed with hydrogen sulphide and the resulting copper sulphide is converted to an equivalent amount of silver sulphide which is darker, easier to compare and more stable. In fact, silver sulphide is compared with silver sulphide ; no copper remains in the rings. Because silver sulphide can be formed in the same way from many other metal ions, it is possible to use only one standard scale consisting of silver sulphide rings for comparison purposes. Silver sulphide is less soluble than most other metal sulphides, hence this procedure is quite generally applicable.

Estimations in which the final comparison is done with silver sulphide can be carried out in still another way. The ion is precipitated in the ring as an insoluble silver salt, which can then be converted to an equivalent amount of silver sulphide by treatment with a sulphide solution of suitable acidity. Chromate and chloride are examples of this procedure, e. g.

$$Cl^- + Ag^+ \rightarrow AgCl,$$

$$\text{and } 2\,AgCl + S^{2-} \rightarrow Ag_2S + 2\,Cl^-$$

It should also be possible to precipitate an ion with a metal which can form a sufficiently insoluble sulphide and finally to transform this metal sulphide into silver sulphide, e. g.

$$SO_4^{2-} \rightarrow PbSO_4 \rightarrow PbS \rightarrow Ag_2S$$

but this would involve an additional step and would include further possible sources of error. Insufficient practical results are available for a decision to be made as to whether this "three-step transformation" would be accurate.

In all cases, the ion in question is finally replaced by an equivalent amount of silver sulphide in the ring, and these silver rings can be compared with a silver sulphide standard scale. In order to keep the conditions as constant as possible, this scale should not be prepared directly from silver nitrate standard solution, but indirectly from another metal ion converted to silver sulphide. Experience has shown that a silver sulphide scale prepared from a copper standard solution is satisfactory. Nevertheless it should be pointed out that other metals could also be used as standards.

The various metals are determined in the following way. Three different rings are prepared from suitable numbers of test drops (see p. 70), the metal ion in these rings is precipitated as sulphide, the metal sulphides are converted to equivalent amounts of silver sulphide and compared with the standard scale. The result is calculated as described previously (p. 73) as if the ion to be determined were copper (assuming that copper has been used as standard metal). This "copper value" must be multiplied by a factor which takes into account the atomic weights and valencies of both the standard metal and the metal to be determined. The general formula for this factor is :

$$\frac{\text{atomic weight of unknown}}{\text{atomic weight of standard}} \times \frac{\text{valency of standard}}{\text{valency of unknown}}$$

which is simply the ratio of the two equivalent weights.

For the semi-quantitative determination of a particular metal ion, the metal must be quantitatively precipitated as sulphide in a stoicheiometrically well-defined form, and the metal sulphide must be completely converted to silver sulphide. It is essential to find out the correct conditions for complete and rapid precipitation, removal of excess sulphide and development with silver nitrate solution.

The following examples give details for the determination of several metal ions with this "universal standard scale".

The preparation of the "universal standard scale"

Wash 1, 2, 4, 6, 8 and 10 drops (1.5 μl) of a copper standard solution (0.1 mg of copper/ml) into the ring zone with 0.05N hydrochloric acid and dry the papers. Soak for 15 minutes in an acid hydrogen sulphide solution (50 ml of saturated hydrogen sulphide water containing 1 drop of concentrated hydrochloric acid). Rinse thoroughly under the tap and finally with distilled water. Develop the rings by immersion for 10 minutes in a 1% silver nitrate solution, wash with distilled water, rinse thoroughly under the tap and dry. This standard scale is stable and its brown-black colour can be easily compared.

Lead or Cadmium

Prepare the rings as described for the standard scale. Before bathing in the hydrogen sulphide solution, fume quickly over ammonia to neutralize the hydrochloric acid.

Bismuth

The sample solution must be sufficiently acid to prevent hydrolysis. Prepare the three sample rings with 0.1N hydrochloric acid, dry, fume over ammonia and develop for 15 minutes in a saturated hydrogen sulphide solution containing about 10% concentrated hydrochloric acid.

To ensure complete precipitation, carry out the sulphide precipitation in a closed glass flask at about 40—50°C. (Caution! Pressure!) Rinse the three rings with distilled water and immerse for 15 minutes in a 1% silver nitrate solution at 40—50°C. Rinse and dry.

Arsenic(III)

Wash the sample drops into the ring zone using $0.01N$ sodium carbonate solution and dry; develop the rings with hydrogen sulphide as described above for the bismuth determination but allow precipitation to proceed for 30 minutes to ensure completion. Wash the sulphide rings well with 1% ammonium nitrate solution and immerse for 15 minutes in 1% silver nitrate solution at 40—50°C. Rinse carefully and dry.

Antimony (III)

The sample solution must be acid enough to avoid hydrolysis (about $3N$ HCl). Develop the dried sample rings for 15 minutes at room temperature in saturated hydrogen sulphide water containing 10% hydrochloric acid. Rinse well and treat for 10 minutes with a 1% silver nitrate solution.

It has been found that good results are obtained if the factor is calculated using a valency of 4 (III to V).

Molybdenum

Prepare the sample rings with ammonia solution (1 : 1) as washing solvent. Fume the dried rings over hydrochloric acid and develop for 20 minutes in slightly acidic hydrogen sulphide water, again in a closed glass flask at 40—50°C as for bismuth and arsenic. Rinse the sulphide rings with 1% ammonium nitrate solution and finally develop in 1% silver nitrate solution.

Cobalt or Nickel

Fume the sample rings over hydrogen sulphide water and then spray with a solution containing 10 ml of ammonium sulphide solution, 100 ml of hydrogen sulphide water and 1 g of ammonium nitrate. Rinse in 1% ammonium nitrate solution, and treat the rings with 1% silver nitrate solution for 10 minutes.

Zinc

Dry the sample rings, fume over ammonia solution and soak for 10 minutes in hydrogen sulphide water containing 2% of sodium acetate

6*

and a small drop of acetic acid. After rinsing with water, develop the rings with 1% silver nitrate solution for 10 minutes.

Manganese (II)

Soak the sample rings for 15 minutes at 40—50°C in a solution containing 100 ml of hydrogen sulphide water, 10 ml of ammonium sulphide and 1 g of ammonium nitrate. After rinsing with 1% ammonium nitrate solution, develop the rings for 15 minutes in 1% silver nitrate solution.

Iron (III)

Immerse the sample rings for 15 minutes in a mixture of 100 ml of hydrogen sulphide water and 10 ml of ammonium sulphide solution, rinse well with distilled water and develop for 5 minutes in a 1% silver nitrate solution.

Calculations:

An example of an iron determination illustrates the calculations. Three rings from 1, 3 and 5 drops of sample solution were compared with the universal standard scale derived from a copper standard solution (0.1 mg of copper/ml). The results were :

Unknown rings	Standard rings	
	"first guess"	"second guess"
1 drop	I—II	2
3 drops	IV—VI	4
5 drops	VIII—X	10
9 drops		16

Thus the "copper value" is $0.1 \times 16/9 = 0.177$, and when the appropriate figures are inserted in the formula, (p. 82), the factor is found to be :

$$f = \frac{Fe}{Cu} \times \frac{2}{3} = 0.585$$

By multiplying the "copper value", 0.177, by the factor, 0.585, the concentration found for the iron solution is 0.104. (The actual concentration was 0.100 mg of iron/ml ; the error was thus only 4%).

Removal of interfering ions Because sulphide is a very unselective reagent, the removal of interfering ions is very important. There are many possibilities for overcoming the interference of other sulphide precipitants ; the most obvious method is to separate them either directly on the paper or previously in the solution, as described in chapter III (p. 79). The right choice of pH for the sulphide precipitation will obviously solve many problems. For example, when cadmium is precipitated from an acid hydrogen sulphide solution, iron, zinc or manganese do not interfere. Masking agents can also prevent interferences in some cases ; thus cadmium can be determined in presence of copper if the solution contains potassium cyanide.[25]

The metal to be determined can be fixed in the ring first with a selective reagent, the interfering ions removed and the precipitated metal transformed into the sulphide. For example, iron in the ring can be fixed with potassium ferrocyanide, after which the paper is rinsed well to remove interfering ions and then bathed in a solution of ammonium sulphide.

One of these possibilities is applicable in most cases.

A very promising application of this technique appears to be inorganic paper chromatography. The single spots of a chromatogram can be cut out and extracted, and the metal ions can be determined in these various extracts. The errors in this analytical procedure have proved to be of the same order as those of the ring colorimetric methods described earlier. As can be seen from the descriptions of the various determinations, the procedures take longer than those using a special standard scale for each ion ; but there are cases, nevertheless, where the use of this universal standard scale is of advantage, as in paper chromatography.

CHAPTER IV

THE RING OVEN METHOD COMBINED WITH OTHER TECHNIQUES

MANY variations are possible in the combination of the ring oven method with other techniques. It has already been mentioned that the silver sulphide standard scale is applicable in the semi-quantitative evaluation of spots in a paper chromatogram ; general ring colorimetry can be used in the same way.

In the case of polarography, the ring oven is only used to separate the different ions ; the determinations themselves are carried out with the polarograph. Sectors of definite size are cut out and the substances concentrated in the line are dissolved and analysed.

On the following pages, some of the major work which has been done by combining the ring oven technique with other procedures is discussed.

A. RING OVEN METHOD AND ELECTROGRAPHY

In the analysis of metallic samples, it is often advantageous to use electric current for dissolution rather than an acid. The sample is made the anode and an aluminium or platinum electrode forms the cathode ; a piece of filter paper moistened with an electrolyte is placed between the electrodes. Some of the metallic specimen is transported to the paper by anodic dissolution. This type of "electrographic analysis" has been described by Fritz[99] and Glazunow.[100]

(1) Qualitative analysis

Stephen[101] has suggested a combination of these electrographic principles with the ring oven method ("ring electrography"). The combined method has proved very useful for the rapid qualitative analysis of many ferrous and non-ferrous metals. The apparatus required is shown in Fig. 14.

It consists of an aluminium rod of about 4 mm diameter, which is contained in an insulating material and acts as a spring plunger. Electrical contact is made when the plunger is pressed into the container, the spring assuring that a minimum pressure is applied. This forms the cathode, while a pointed steel probe forms the anode. The two electrodes are connected to a source of low voltage (3 volts from a dry battery); a rheostat and a milliameter can be inserted in the circuit in order to control the current.

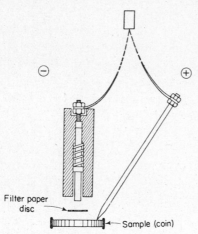

Fig. 14. Electrographic sampling

An analysis of a metal surface, for example of a plated article, a coin, etc., is carried out as follows.

Procedure: Clean the surface with a mild abrasive in order to ensure good contact. Punch out a small disc of filter paper with a 9-mm stainless steel punch, moisten it with a suitable electrolyte (sodium chloride, sodium nitrate, etc.) and place on the part to be examined. Place the cathode on the disc and apply pressure to the spring of the plunger. Complete the electric circuit by bringing the anode into contact with the metal surface. Pass a current of 10-50 milliamps for 2—3 seconds and then remove the cathode.

The filter disc now contains metal ions derived from the metal specimen, and its further treatment follows the usual qualitative ring oven method. Place the disc in the centre of a round filter and treat it as if it were a normal test drop. Apply some suitable separation scheme as described in Chapter II.

This method of sampling is rapid and, for all practical purposes, non-destructive. Because only a few micrograms (3—5) of metal need be removed from an area of about 12 mm² (the diameter of the cathode being about 4 mm), the attack on the specimen surface is scarcely apparent. The technique is therefore very well suited to investigations of *objets d'art*, coins, statuettes, etc. It has been used to analyse copper base alloys (such as aluminium bronze, manganese bronze, German silver and cupronickel coinage), nickel alloys (such as Monel and Nichrome) and iron alloys (such as alloy steel, Nilo K, Invar etc.). Because commoner alloys have seldom more than four or five constituents, a very simplified qualitative scheme suffices in most cases ; a complete analysis is therefore obtainable in a few minutes.

For this procedure, the name "electro-ring-testing" has been proposed.

(2) Semi-quantitative analysis

The combination of spot colorimetry with the ring oven has led to a convenient procedure for semi-quantitative electrographic analysis. For quantitative application of electrographic sampling, it is of course essential that the ratio of the different metals electrotransferred to the filter paper disc is the same as in the alloy itself.

Glazunow (1929)[100] states that proportionate solution of the metal components occurs only if the alloy is a solid solution ; when more than one phase is present, each has its special solution potential. It has, however, been shown that the various phase potentials of a polyphase alloy have less effect on the relative solution rates of the components in each phase if the potential applied in the sampling procedure is increased.

The semi-quantitative analysis of some simple alloys can thus be carried out with experimentally established conditions for the anodic dissolution, and ring colorimetry for the evaluation of the electrographs. It is thus possible to carry out an analysis without using a balance at all. Although drop numbers are not involved, the time of electrolysis can be varied.

An example of a semi-quantitative electrographic analysis of Invar, a binary alloy containing 64% of iron and 36% of nickel serves to illustrate the technique.

Procedure: Take three electrographs from the cleaned surface of the sample as described in the qualitative procedure. Keep the current constant but alter the time of the current flow in regular steps. It is advisable to carry out one or two qualitative tests before the three electrographs are taken for the actual determination, in order to decide about suitable times and currents.

Place the three discs on round filters and wash the iron and nickel in each disc into the ring zone with $0.1N$ hydrochloric acid. Dry the three filter papers and cut them in halves. On one half of the papers, develop iron with potassium ferrocyanide, and on the other set, precipitate nickel with dimethylglyoxime and remove iron(III) hydroxide by rinsing in tartrate solution (cf. p. 79). Then compare the semicircles with iron and nickel standard scales.

Calculation: The three different electrographs are named A, B and C ; no "drop numbers" are of course known. The standard solutions of iron or nickel contained 0.1 mg/ml of the required ion. Assume that the following correspondence with standard rings has been established by the procedure described on p. 73.

Electrograph	Fe	Ni
A	2	2
B	5	3
C	9	6
	16	11

To calculate the percentages of the two metals, it is assumed that their sum is 100%. Thus :

$$16 \times 0.1 + 11 \times 0.1 = 2.7 = 100\%$$

$$\text{and } Fe = \frac{16 \times 0.1}{2.7} \times 100 \qquad = 59.25\% \ (64\%)$$

$$Ni = \frac{11 \times 0.1}{2.7} \times 100 \qquad = 40.75\% \ (36\%)$$

As in most indirect analytical procedures, the range of error is greater than in the direct method, but it still lies within the limits tolerable for a semi-quantitative procedure. Simple alloys with two, three or even four components, such as Nilo K (Fe, Co, Ni), German silver (Cu, Ni, Zn) and cupronickel coinage (Cu, Ni), can be analysed very rapidly by similar procedures. This method, for which the name "electro-ring-colorimetry" has been proposed, seems well suited to the classification of alloy types.

(3) Sorting of steels

The electrographic sampling technique and the ring oven method have also been combined by Nall and Scholey,[102] who described a non-destructive microchemical method of sorting steels.

The method can be applied to the rapid analysis of carbon and low alloy steels. Manganese, nickel, molybdenum and chromium are estimated ; only 2 or 3 of the components need usually be estimated to decide the type of the steel. This method was specially developed for BRITISH STANDARD STEELS, but could readily be modified for other steels or even other alloys. The purpose of the analysis is simply to decide to which type of a limited number of possibilities the particular steel belongs. When the ring oven is used, lengthy chemical analyses or more elaborate techniques such as spectrography and magnetic-electrical sorting can be avoided.

The time of electrolysis is always 20 seconds, and an electrographic sampler with a 3 V torch battery is used. The sampler admits a 5.5 cm filter paper, the centre of which is moistened with a suitable electrolyte. A spring-loaded graphite counter electrode serves as cathode ; this ensures a reproducible pressure, as in the electrographic sampler described earlier (p. 88).

Only one ring is prepared for the determination of each of the four above mentioned steel components, instead of the three rings usual in ring-colorimetry ; in this particular case, a decision can be made with only one ring.

Nickel and molybdenum can be determined in one ring so that only three electrographs need be taken for an analysis. These rings are then compared with rings made under the same conditions from standard steels containing known percentages of the different metals. Five standard steels covering the range of percentages of manganese, nickel, chromium and molybdenum are sufficient as a basis for classification.

Iron from the steel interferes in the estimation of manganese and nickel, and is separated by using ammonia solution for washing into the ring zone ; ferric hydroxide is thus fixed in the central spot.

The following Table 7 summarizes the electrolytes used for the sampling procedure and the reactions employed for developing the metal ions after their concentration in a ring zone. For further details about the various determinations the original publication should be consulted.

Table 7. SORTING OF STEELS

Element	Electrolyte	Reaction	Colour
Mn	0.5N HCl	Potassium periodate/tetra-base	blue
Ni	0.5N HCl	Dimethylglyoxime	red
Cr	6.4N HNO$_3$ (s. g. 1. 20)	ox. $\rightarrow$ CrO$_4^{2-}$; $+$ AgNO$_3$	yellow-orange
Mo	1N HCl	Ammonium thiocyanate/stannous chloride	orange-red

This method of sorting steels is used as a routine technique and has proved satisfactory in field trials where it is often necessary to decide quickly the composition of steels.

B. RADIOCHEMICAL APPLICATIONS

The ring oven method can also be applied to radioactive substances.[103] Its convenience for handling extremely small quantities is advantageous not only because of the normal scarcity of the sample available, but because the security precautions necessary with radioactive substances are simplified.

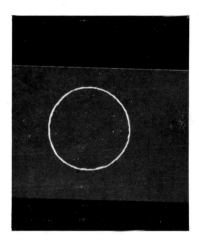

FIG. 15. Ring-autoradiograph of 0.01 μc ^{32}P

Radioactive substances are detected in a ring zone by autoradiography, which does not require elaborate apparatus and provides a permanent record. The radioactive substances are concentrated in a sharp ring zone in the usual way. This is particularly useful in autoradiography, because the degree of blackening of the film depends on the activity per unit area rather than on the total activity present.

For example, one drop of a phosphate solution containing approximately 0.01 μc. ^{32}P is washed into a ring zone, soaked in magnesia mixture solution to fix the phosphate, rinsed well and dried. The paper with the magnesium ammonium phosphate ring is then placed in contact with a film (e. g. X-ray, Ilford, Industrial G) and held with a glass plate. After 12 hours, the film is developed and a very distinct ring is obtained (Fig. 15).

This method can be used to identify very small amounts of active substances. It is necessary to know which active substances could be present ; then a solution containing an inactive mixture of the ions possibly present in an active form is added as carrier and a normal chemical separation scheme is carried out. After the different sectors have been rinsed thoroughly, they are placed in contact with a film. Only sectors corresponding to active ions can give an autoradiograph. The most serious problem is, of course, co-precipitation, but this must be also circumvented in larger scale analyses. The difficulty can be overcome by the methods normally applied in tracer analysis.

As an example of such an identification, consider a test drop which is known to contain labelled sulphate, phosphate or iodide or combinations of these ions. A drop of an inactive mixture of the three ions is added. One drop of the resulting solution is washed into the ring zone and dried. Three sectors are cut out and treated with precipitating reagents. Barium chloride solution precipitates sulphate on one sector, magnesia mixture fixes phosphate on the second, and silver nitrate solution fixes iodide on the third. The three sectors are washed, dried and placed in contact with a film. If only the barium sulphate ring gives an autoradiograph, then the only active component is sulphate.

A counting device such as a Geiger-Müller counter can also be used to determine the activity in a particular sector. Anti-kainen[62] has suggested the determination of ^{233}U by alpha-counting in the ring zone after the isolation of uranium from other active materials (cf. p. 65). It seems likely that auto-radiography could also provide a method for the semi-quanti-tative determination of active substances in combination with the ring oven method.

C. THE RING OVEN AS EXTRACTOR

The ring oven can be used as an extractor for very minute quantities of test material.[104]

Little more need be said about the extraction of liquid samples because all that is done with the ring oven is in fact extrac-

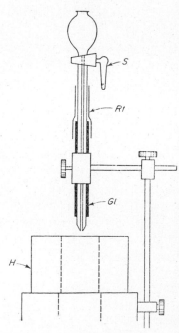

FIG. 16. Adjustment for continuous extraction

tion. The drop which is to be extracted is placed on a filter paper and all the soluble substances are washed by a suitable extraction solvent into the ring zone. For example, butter fat in a drop of milk can be extracted with a mixture of ether—ethanol (1 : 1) and a translucent ring of 22 mm diameter appears on the paper.

For the extraction of solid substances, a hollow is pressed into the centre of a moistened filter paper by means of a thick fire-polished glass rod and the paper is dried. The sample to be extracted is placed in this hollow and covered with a small filter disc. The extraction is then carried out in the usual way on the ring oven. For example, sulphur can be extracted with carbon disulphide from a minute sample of a pesticide. When organic solvents are applied, the temperature of the ring oven must be adjusted to several degrees above the boiling point of the extracting solvent.

It is thus possible to extract extremely small quantities in a very simple manner. The extracted parts concentrate in a sharply outlined zone where they can be identified. This procedure appears well suited to the rapid assay of crude drugs and related pharmaceutical materials, for spot tests for many of these substances are now known (see, e. g., F. Feigl, *Spot Tests in Organic Analysis*, Elsevier, Amsterdam 1958). This method could also be valuable in criminological investigations.

For continuous extraction[76] with organic solvents, a capillary pipette attached to a dropping funnel can be used as shown in Fig. 16. This pipette is held in position in the guiding glass tube, *Gl*, by means of a short piece of rubber tubing, *Rt*, which prevents the heavy pipette from destroying the filter paper. The stopcock *S* has to be carefully adjusted in order to regulate the flow of liquid. This pipette is advantageous when a prolonged extraction procedure is necessary.

D. The Ring Oven and Paper Chromatography

The ring oven method is not a paper chromatographic method (compare p. 33), but there are several ways in which these two techniques can be combined. For example, one method could be used for a preliminary separation, the various components from the spots, or rings, could be extracted, and the second technique applied for final separation. It would also be possible to use a chromatographic method for separation and the ring oven method for semi-quantitative determination of the substances after extraction from the various spots of the chromatogram. The possible application of a silver sulphide universal standard scale has already been mentioned in this connection (p. 85).

Apart from these obvious combinations of the two methods, two other recent applications of the ring oven technique in paper chromatography[105] should be mentioned here, although very little experience has been gained in the use of these methods. The increasing interest of analytical chemists in inorganic paper chromatography[106] justifies their description.

On a one-dimensional chromatogram, the spots obtained always cover bigger areas than the original sample drop, which means, that the concentration of separated substances per unit area becomes much smaller. Thus in order to finish with a sufficient concentration for an identification reaction the amounts of individual sample components must be considerably above the identification limit. The ring oven method can prove useful in these situations.

A one-dimensional chromatogram is run on a paper strip, but before the various identification reactions are applied, the paper strip is placed on the ring oven and rings are washed in the usual way. The first ring is centred at the start point and successive rings are made 22 mm apart (i. e. the exact diameter of the ring oven bore-hole) through the whole length of the chromatogram. When the solvent mixture used for developing the chromatogram contains mineral acids, it is necessary to fume the paper strip over ammonia to neutralize the acid before the strip is placed on the ring oven ; otherwise the paper could be destroyed. The liquid used for washing the rings (dilute acetic acid, $0.1N$ hydrochloric acid, etc.) must be one in which the various chromatographed substances are soluble.

In this way the substances contained in the various spots of the chromatogram are concentrated in circular arcs or rings, whose position depends on the points from where the rings were washed. The separated substances are thus much more highly concentrated than in the chromatograph spots and, in fact, more concentrated than in the original sample drop (see p. 19).

After the strip has been cut longitudinally into two halves, the different ring-arcs are located on one half by spraying with suitable reagents. The other half is used for more detailed study. The different R_F-values can be readily evaluated from the dimensions and positions of the different arcs. Figure 17 illustrates the whole procedure.

It should be possible to run chromatograms with much smaller samples ; in this way, a better separation would be obtained, or the path-length would be shorter and therefore less time would be required.

In the second possible combination of the ring oven and chromatography, paper chromatography around a circle is used instead of the ascending or descending method. This type of chromatography is different from that known as radial or circular chromatography.

The filter paper is shaped as shown in Fig. 18. *A* is the starting point ; the outer diameter is 15 mm and the inner diameter 7 mm. The average path-length is therefore about 35 mm. Obviously only extremely small samples can be used ; if such samples were used in ordinary chromatography, the spots finally produced would be so dilute that they could no longer be detected. The sample droplet is applied with an extremely narrow capillary. The paper ring is placed on a glass hook on the lid of a weighing vessel (Fig. 19), and the tail is dipped into the solvent mixture used to develop the chromatogram. After a few minutes — three to ten minutes, depending on the solvent used — the solvent front reaches the end of the circular paper strip. The paper is then dried, the tail is cut off (Fig. 18, dotted line) and the remaining filter paper ring is placed on a round filter. In order to achieve a proper contact between the ring and the supporting filter, the paper ring must be fixed with a synthetic glue or a cellulose acetate-acetone slurry. Only a very little glue (small dots) should be applied to avoid blocking the capillaries of the filter paper. A small filter paper disc (8 mm diameter) is also glued on to the ring in order to "bridge" the 7 mm hole of the paper ring. Figure 20 illustrates the very simple procedure.

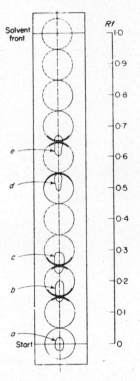

The prepared filter with the ring is placed on the ring oven and all (separated) substances are washed into the ring zone of the underlying filter with a suitable liquid ; essentially, the different spots are "projected" into the ring. Because of the concentrating effect, the various substances in the ring zone have a concentration which permits their detection. The result is a

Fig. 17. Illustration of the combination of conventional one-dimensional paper chromatography with the ring oven method

ring, different parts of which contain the various chromatographed substances owing to their different R_F-values.

For example, a chromatogram can be prepared in this way from one drop of solution containing altogether about 0.07 μg

of copper, cobalt and nickel, which covers an area of 2 mm diameter. Acetone—hydrochloric acid—water (85 : 10 : 5) is used
to develop the chromatogram in 3 minutes. Then the substances
are washed into the ring zone with 0.05 N hydrochloric acid.

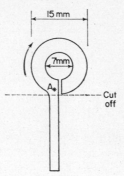

FIG. 18. Circular filter paper strip

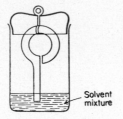

FIG. 19. Adjustment for developing a paper chromatogram
along a circle

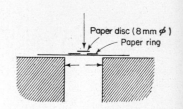

FIG. 20. Transfer of the separated substances from the chromatogram into the ring zone

The filter is dried, fumed over ammonia and sprayed with an
alcoholic solution of dithio-oxamide. The resulting ring has the
distribution : nickel (violet), cobalt (brown) and copper (grey-
green).

It should be emphasized that the papers used for the two
methods described above must be very pure because any impurities would also be concentrated in the ring zone (compare
p. 67). The main contaminations in filter paper are iron and
copper. This must be taken into account, especially when extre-

mely small samples are used as in the last method. Because the sizes of the filter paper used in this method are very small compared with those in normal paper chromatography, the filter paper can be either a high grade commercial paper or a specially purified one.

So far, only a little experience has been gained with these methods and only inorganic samples have been examined, but there is little doubt that organic samples could also be treated in this way. Naturally, samples containing many components would cause trouble, but there are quite a few cases where the combination of the ring oven method with this type of circular paper chromatography would be of advantage, e. g. in systematic qualitative analysis. A ring oven with a larger bore-hole would probably allow greater flexibility, because a larger path-length on the chromatogram would be available.

Conclusion

The many different possibilities of the ring oven method have been shown in this monograph. As with any recently developed technique, much work remains to be done in developing refinements and extending practical applications.

In qualitative analysis, more chemical reactions can be applied for the detection of ions on the ring oven. For particular purposes special analytical schemes must be worked out. A scheme for the identification of anion mixtures in a single drop is now being developed.

In semi-quantitative analysis, the method must be extended to cover more metallic and non-metallic ions. In combination with auto-radiography the ring oven method might be suitable for the semi-quantitative determination of radioactive substances; preliminary experiments in this direction are promising.

The ring oven technique should find extensive application in the air-pollution field, which is becoming more and more important in industrial countries.

The ring oven method, and especially its combination with paper chromatography should provide new possibilities not only in the inorganic field but also in the examination of organic substances.

The author would be grateful to receive all available information from colleagues who are using any of these methods and would be glad to enter into any discussion or correspondence which would further the development of this technique.

LIST OF RING OVEN PUBLICATIONS

1. H. Weisz : "Ausführung von Trennungen in einem Tropfen", *Mikrochim. Acta (Wien)*, **1954**, 140.
2. H. Weisz : "Ein Trennungsgang in einem Tropfen", *Mikrochim. Acta (Wien)*, **1954**, 376.
3. H. Weisz : "Zur Tüpfelkolorimetrie", *Mikrochim. Acta (Wien)*, **1954**, 460.
4. H. Weisz : "Anwendung des Ringofens in der Tüpfelkolorimetrie", *Mikrochim. Acta (Wien)*, **1954**, 785.
5. H. Weisz : "Separating Ions in a Single Drop", *Chemical Age*, **1954**, 1039.
6. H. Weisz : "Inquiries on Old Egyptian Bronzes", *J. Chem. Ed.*, **32**, 70 (1955).
7. C. A. Bank und W. van der Eijk : "Micro-druppelanalyse van Kationen volgens de methode van Weisz", *Chem. Weekblad*, **51**, 351 (1955).
8. H. Weisz : "Die Ringofenmethode", *Mikrochim. Acta (Wien)*, **1956**, 667.
9. L. C. F. Blackman : "Separation and Identification of Molybdenum and Tungsten", *Mikrochim. Acta (Wien)*, **1956**, 1366.
10. W. I. Stephen : "The Use of the Weisz Ring Oven in Electrographic Analysis", *Mikrochim. Acta (Wien)*, **1956**, 1531.
11. W. I. Stephen : "Contribution to Spot Colorimetry using the Weisz Ring Oven", *Mikrochim. Acta (Wien)*, **1956**, 1540.
12. W. R. Nall and R. Scholey : "A Non-destructive Microchemical Method of Sorting Steels", *Metallurgia*, **1956**, 97.
13. H. Weisz and F. Scott : "The Application of the Ring-Oven Technique to Radio-active Substances", *Mikrochim. Acta (Wien)*, **1956**, 1856.
14. A. Vioque : "Elementos trazas en grasas comestibles. III. Aplicaciones de la microtechnica de la estufa anular de Weisz", *Grasas y Aceites*, **7**, 195 (1956).

104   LIST OF RING OVEN PUBLICATIONS

15. H. Weisz : "Detection of Impurities in Filter Paper by the Ring Oven Method", *Analyst*, **82**, 132 (1957).
16. W. Knödel und H. Weisz : "Mathematisches zur kolorimetrischen Analyse mit dem Ringofen", *Mikrochim. Acta, (Wien)*, **1957**, 417.
17. L. Serrano-Berges : "Separacion de iones en una gota usando la Estufa Anular de Weisz", *Inform. Quim. Anal.* **11**, 13 (1957).
18. W. I. Stephen : "Ring-Microchemistry, A New Analytical Method" Waverley Gold Medal Essay, *Research*, **10**, 429 (1957).
19. H. Ballczo und H. Weisz : "Zum Nachweis des Fluorions", *Mikrochim. Acta, (Wien)*, **1957**, 751.
20. H. Weisz, M. Ćelap und V. Almazan : "Ringofen-Tüpfelkolorimetrie mit Hilfe einer Silbersulfid-Standardskala", *Mikrochim. Acta (Wien)*, **1959**, 36.
21. P. W. West and A. K. Mukherji : "Separation and Microidentification of Metallic Ions Employing Solvent Extraction and Ring Oven Techniques", *Anal. Chem.*, **31**, 947 (1959).
22. P. J. Antikainen : "Separation and Determination of Micro-Amounts of Uranium in the Presence of Th, Bi and Pb using Ring Oven", *Suomen Kem.*, **B31**, 277 (1958).
23. H. Ballczo : "Eine Erweiterung der Ringofenmethode", *Mikrochim. Acta, (Wien)*, **1959**, 314.
24. P. W. West : in *"Trace Analysis"*, J. H. Yoe and H. J. Koch (Editors), Wiley, New York, 1957, p. 165.
25. P. J. Antikainen: "Separation, Qualitative and Semiquantitative Determination of Micro-Amounts of Nickel and Cobalt by the Weisz Ring Oven Method", *Mikrochim. Acta (Wien)* **1959**, 558.
26. H. Ballczo und M. Hodos: "Sulfatnachweis in einem Tropfen unter Anwendung des Ringofens aus Glas." *Mikrochim. Acta (Wien)* **1960**, 267.

REFERENCES

1. F. Feigl, *Mikrochemie*, **2**, 187 (1924).
2. H. Weisz, *Mikrochim. Acta (Wien)*, **1954**, 140.
3. H. Ballczo, *Mikrochim. Acta (Wien)*, **1959**, 314.
4. H. Weisz, *Mikrochim. Acta (Wien)*, **1954**, 376.
5. C. J. van Nieuwenburg and J. W. van Ligten, Private communication.
6. R. Strebinger and H. Holzer, *Mikrochemie*, **8**, 264 (1930).
7. F. Feigl and H. A. Suter, *Ind. Eng. Chem. Anal. Ed.*, **14**, 840 (1942).
8. F. Feigl and P. Krumholz, *Ber.* **62**, 1138 (1929).
9. F. Feigl and V. Gentil, *Mikrochim. Acta (Wien)*, **1954**, 90.
10. E. Eegriwe, *Z. anal. Chem.*, **70**, 400 (1927).
11. F. Feigl and V. Gentil, Unpublished studies, cited in *Spot Tests*, 5th ed., p. 105.
12. P. W. West and W. C. Hamilton, *Anal. Chem.*, **24**, 1025 (1952).
13. Pr. Ray, *Z. anal. Chem.*, **79**, 94 (1929).
14. F. Feigl, *Mikrochemie*, **1**, 76 (1923).
15. E. van Dalen and G. de Vries, *Anal. Chim. Acta*, **3**, 567 (1949).
16. F. Feigl and R. Stern, *Z. anal. Chem.*, **60**, 31 (1921).
17. L. Tschugaeff, *Ber.*, **38**, 2520 (1905).
18. P. Cazeneuve, *Compt. rend.*, **131**, 346 (1900).
19. N. A. Tananaeff and I. Tananaeff, *Z. anorg. allgem. Chem.*, **170**, 118 (1928).
20. F. Feigl, *Z. anal. Chem.*, **60**, 24 (1921).
21. P. Krumholz and J. V. Sanchez, *Mikrochemie*, **15**, 114 (1934).
22. F. Goppelsroeder, *Z. anal. Chem.*, **7**, 195 (1868).
23. N. A. Tananaeff and G. A. Pantschenko, *Z. anorg. allgem. Chem.*, **150**, 163 (1926).
24. C. A. Bank and W. van der Eijk, *Chem. Weekblad*, **51**, 351 (1955).
25. W. I. Stephen, *S. E. R. L. Tech. J. (Baldock, England)*, **5**, 47 (1955).
26. P. W. West and A. K. Mukherji, *Anal. Chem.*, **31**, 947 (1959).

106   REFERENCES

27. G. H. Morrison and H. Freiser, *Solvent Extraction in Analytical Chemistry*, Wiley, New York, 1957.
28. J. K. Carlton, *Anal. Chem.*, **22**, 1072 (1950).
29. F. Feigl, *Z. anal. Chem,.* **74**, 380 (1928).
30. N. A. Tananaeff and I. Tananaeff, *Z. anorg. allgem. Chem.*, **170**, 120 (1928).
31. N. A. Tananaeff, *Z. anorg. allgem. Chem.*, **140**, 320 (1924).
32. F. Feigl and F. Neuber, *Z. anal. Chem.*, **62**, 370 (1923).
33. N. A. Tananaeff, *Z. anorg. allgem. Chem.*, **136**, 373 (1924); **140**, 321 (1924).
34. H. Wölbling and B. Steiger, *Z. angew. Chem.*, **46**, 279 (1933).
35. K. Heller and P. Krumholz, *Mikrochemie*, **7**, 214 (1929).
36. E. Léger, *Z. anal. Chem.*, **28**, 374 (1889).
37. L. Vanino and F. Treubert, *Ber.*, **31**, 1113 (1898).
38. L. Kulberg, *Mikrochemie*, **20**, 153 (1936).
39. J. Hoste, *Anal. Chim. Acta*, **4**, 23 (1950).
40. F. L. Hahn and G. Leimbach, *Ber.*, **55**, 3070 (1922).
41. F. Feigl and L. I. Miranda, *Ind. Eng. Chem., Anal. Ed.*, **16**, 141 (1944).
42. F. P. Dwyer, *Australian Chem. Inst. J. and Proc.*, **4**, 26 (1937).
43. L. C. F. Blackman, *Mikrochim. Acta (Wien)*, **1956**, 1366.
44. L. Spiegel and Th. Maass, *Ber.*, **36**, 512 (1903).
45. F. Feigl, *Spot Tests*, 5th ed., Elsevier, Amsterdam, 1958.
46. N. A. Tananaeff and G. A. Pantschenko, *Chem. Abstracts*, **24**, 567 (1930).
47. J. Meyer and A. Pawletta, *Z. anal. Chem.*, **69**, 15 (1926).
48. G. Malatesta and E. di Nola, *Chem. Abstracts*, **8**, 1397 (1914).
49. H. Holzer, *Mikrochemie*, **8**, 275 (1930); F. Feigl, P. Krumholz and E. Rajmann, *Ibid.* 165 (1931).
50. N. A. Tananaeff and G. T. Michaltschischin, *Z. anal. Chem.*, **94**, 188 (1933).
51. Pr. Ray and R. M. Ray, *Quart. J. Indian Chem. Soc.*, **3**, 118 (1926); Pr. Ray, *Z. anal. Chem.*, **79**, 94 (1929).
52. H. Ditz, *Chem. Ztg.*, **25**, 110 (1901); **46**, 121 (1922); *Z. anorg. allgem. Chem.*, **219**, 97 (1934); I. M. Kolthoff, *Mikrochemie*, **8**, 176 (1930).
53. F. Feigl and A. Caldas, *Anal. Chem.*, **29**, 580 (1957).
54. J. H. Yoe, *J. Am. Chem. Soc.*, **54**, 4139 (1932).
55. R. Belcher, A. J. Nutten and W. I. Stephen, *Analyst*, **76**, 903 (1951).
56. L. P. Hammett and C. T. Sottery, *J. Am. Chem. Soc.*, **47**, 142 (1925).
57. F. W. Attack, *J. Soc. Chem. Ind.*, **34**, 936 (1935); K. Heller and P. Krumholz, *Mikrochemie*, **7**, 221 (1929).
58. W. I. Stephen, *Mikrochim. Acta (Wien)*, **1956**, 1540.

59. F. FEIGL and D. GOLDSTEIN, Unpublished studies, cited in *Spot Tests*, 1. c, p. 191.
60. K. A. HOFMANN, *Ber.*, **45**, 2480 (1912).
61. F. FEIGL, P. KRUMHOLZ and E. RAJMANN, *Mikrochemie*, **9**, 395 (1931).
62. P. J. ANTIKAINEN, *Suomen Kem.*, **B 31**, 277 (1958).
63. F. FEIGL and R. STERN, *Z. anal. Chem.*, **60**, 39 (1921).
64. F. FEIGL, *Mikrochemie*, **2**, 188 (1924).
65. F. FEIGL and S. PICKHOLZ, Unpublished studies, cited in *Spot Tests*, 1. c., p. 221.
66. H. WEISZ, *Mikrochim. Acta (Wien)*, **1959**, 32.
67. see F. FEIGL, *Spot Tests*, 1. c., p. 225.
68. F. HAHN, H. WOLF and G. JAEGER, *Ber.*, **57** 1394 (1924).
69. I. M. KOLTHOFF, *Z. anal. Chem.*, **70**, 398 (1927).
70. G. WITTIG and co-workers, *Ann.*, **563**, 114, 118, 126 (1949).
71. N. S. POLUEKTOFF, *Mikrochemie*, **14**, 265 (1933—34).
72. H. WEISZ, *Mikrochim. Acta (Wien)*, **1956**, 1225.
73. D. GANASSINI, *Chem. Zentr.*, **1904**, I, 1172.
74. F. FEIGL, *Spot Tests*, 1. c., p. 265.
75. G. GUTZEIT, *Helv. Chim. Acta*, **12**, 713 (1929).
76. H. BALLCZO and H. WEISZ, *Mikrochim. Acta (Wien)*, **1957**, 751.
77. F. FEIGL, *Rec. trav. chim.*, **58**, 477 (1939).
78. L. N. LAPIN, *Chem. Abstracts*, **35**, 4305 (1941).
79. F. FEIGL, *Rec. trav. chim.*, **58**, 478 (1939).
80. A. L. GOTTLIEB, *Chem. Abstracts*, **32**, 4469 (1938).
81. J. BLOM, *Ber.*, **59**, 121 (1926).
82. P. GRIESS, *Ber.*, **12**, 427 (1879).
83. F. FEIGL, *Z. anal. Chem.*, **61**, 454 (1922); **74**, 386 (1928); **77**, 299 (1929).
84. F. W. DAUBE, *Ber.*, **3**, 609 (1870).
85. B. J. MACNULTY *et al.*, *Anal. Chim. Acta*, **14**, 368, 452 (1956).
86. H. WEISZ, *J. Chem. Ed.*, **32**, 70 (1955).
87. A. VIOQUE, *Grasas y Aceites*, **7**, 195 (1956).
88. P. W. WEST, J. H. YOE and H. J. KOCH, JR., *Trace analysis*, (Chapter V), Wiley, New York, 1957.
89. P. W. WEST, in *Air Pollution Training Course Manual*, Public Health Service, U. S. Department of Health, Education and Welfare.
90. E. ABRAHAMCZIK, *Chemie*, **55**, 233 (1942).
91. H. WEISZ, *Analyst*, **82**, 132 (1957).
92. H. WEISZ, Studies with J. Drabner, Dissertation.
93. F. FEIGL, *Z. anal. Chem.*, **152**, 52 (1956).
94. H. YAGODA, *Ind. Eng. Chem., Anal. Ed.*, **9**, 79 (1937).
95. H. WEISZ, *Mikrochim. Acta (Wien)*, **1954**, 460.
96. H. WEISZ, *Mikrochim. Acta (Wien)*, **1954**, 785.

97. W. KNÖDEL and H. WEISZ, *Mikrochim. Acta (Wien)*, **1957**, 417.
98. H. WEISZ, M. B. ĆELAP and V. ALMAŽAN, *Mikrochim. Acta (Wien)*, **1959**, 36.
99. H. FRITZ, *Z. anal. Chem.*, **78**, 418 (1929).
100. A. GLAZUNOW, *Chim. et Ind.*, Spec. No., **1929**, 425.
101. W. I. STEPHEN, *Mikrochim. Acta (Wien)*, **1956**, 1531.
102. W. R. NALL and R. SCHOLEY, *Metallurgia*, **1956**, 97.
103. H. WEISZ and F. SCOTT, *Mikrochim. Acta (Wien)*, **1956**, 1856.
104. H. WEISZ, *Mikrochim. Acta (Wien)*, **1956**, 674.
105. H. WEISZ, Unpublished studies.
106. H. POLLARD and J. F. W. McCOMBE, *Chromatographic Methods of Inorganic Analysis*, Butterworth's Scientific Publications, London, 1956.

SUBJECT INDEX

For authors' names please consult the Lists of References and of ring oven publications.

Acetylacetonate 47
Air pollution 66
Alizarin S 53, 59, 77
Aluminium
  determination of 77
  identification of 41, 42, 53, 59
  separation of 34, 36, 45, 47
Aluminon 53, 59
Ammonium molybdate 62, 63
Aniline 49, 51, 57, 58
Antimony
  determination of 83
  identification of 38, 42, 51, 58
  separation of 34, 36, 47
Area of the ring 19
Arsenic
  determination of 83
  identification of 44, 51, 58
  separation of 43, 47
Autoradiography 93

Barium
  identification of 54, 59
  separation of 45, 47
Benzidine 40, 42, 50, 52, 53, 57, 58, 59, 60, 62, 63
Benzoinoxime 39, 50, 57, 77
Beryllium
  determination of 78
  identification of 53, 59
  separation of 44, 47
Bismuth
  determination of 82

Bismuth
  identification of 37, 42, 50, 57
  separation of 34, 36, 47
Borate
  identification of 62, 63
British Standard Steels 91
Bromate
  identification of 60, 63
Bromide
  identification of 56, 63

Cadion 51, 57
Cadmium
  determination of 77, 82
  identification of 39, 42, 50, 51, 57
  separation of 34, 36, 47
Calcium
  identification of 54, 59
  separation of 45, 47
Capillary sample pipette 22
Capillary washing pipette 16
Centering of the washing pipette 16
Cerium
  separation of 47
Chromate
  identification of 62, 63
Chromazurol S 60, 63, 64
Chromium
  determination of 92
  identification of 40, 42, 53, 58
  separation of 34, 36, 45, 47
Chromotropic acid 41, 42, 53, 59
Cinchonine 50, 57

Cobalt
    determination of 76, 83
    identification of 39, 42, 52, 58
    separation of 34, 36, 45, 47
Confined spot test paper 70
Copper
    determination of 77
    identification of 39, 42, 50, 57
    separation of 34, 36, 47
"Copper value" 82
Corrosion products 66
Criminology 66
Cuproin 50, 57
Curcuma see turmeric

Diethyldithiocarbamate 47
Dihydroxytartaric acid osazone 54, 59
p-Dimethylaminoazophenyl-
    arsonic acid 54, 59
p-Dimethylaminobenzylidene-
    rhodanine 49, 52, 57, 58
Dimethylglyoxime 40, 42, 52, 58, 76
Dimethylnaphthidine 50, 53, 59, 78
Diphenylbenzidine 50
Diphenylcarbazide 40, 42, 49, 53, 57, 58, 62, 63
Dipicrylamine 55, 59, 78
α—α-Dipyridyl 52, 58
2,2'-Diquinolyl see Cuproin
Dithio-oxamide 39, 42, 50, 52, 57, 58, 77
Dithizone 49, 57

Electrography 87
    qualitative 88
    semiquantitative 89
"Electro-ring-colorimetry" 91
Extraction, liquid-liquid 45, 47
    on the ring oven 94
Extraction pipette 46

Ferricyanide
    identification of 60, 63

Ferrocyanide
    identification of 60, 63
Ferron 52, 58
Ferrous dipyridyliodide 50, 57
Filter paper
    black 54, 78
    for ring oven work 17
    impurities in, determination 67
Fluorescein 56, 61, 63
Fluoride
    identification of 60, 62, 63, 64
Foodstuffs 66

Gallium
    separation of 47
Gas generator 20
Germanium
    separation of 47
Glass fibre filter 68
Glass holder 22
Glass ring oven 16, 30
Gold
    identification of 52, 58
    separation of 47
Gutzeit test 51, 58

Hexanitrodiphenylamine see di-
    picrylamine
Hydrogen sulphide
    precipitations with 20
8-Hydroxyquinoline-7-iodo-5-
    sulphonic acid see Ferron

Indium
    separation of 47
Interfering ions, removal 79, 84
Iodate
    identification of 61, 63
Iodide
    identification of 60, 63
Iron
    determination of 72
    identification of 39, 42, 52, 58
    separation of 34, 36, 45, 47

Lead
    determination of 82
    identification of 37, 42, 49, 57
    separation of 34, 36, 47

Magnesium
    determination of 78
    identification of 54, 59
    separation of 44, 45, 47
Manganese
    determination of 84, 92
    identification of 40, 42, 53, 59
    separation of 34, 36, 45, 47
Mercury
    identification of 49, 57
    separation of 43, 44, 47
Mercury thiocyanate 40, 42, 53, 59
Molybdenum
    determination of 83, 92
    identification of 51, 58
    separation of 47, 64
Morin 38, 41, 42, 51, 53, 58, 59

a-Naphthylamine 61, 63
Nickel
    determination of 76, 83, 92
    identification of 40, 42, 52, 58
    separation of 34, 36, 45, 47
Nioxime 52
Nitrate
    identification of 61, 63
Nitrite
    identification of 61, 63
p-Nitrobenzeneazoresorcinol 54, 59
a-Nitroso-β-naphthol 39, 42, 52, 58
    76

Objets d'art 66, 89
Oils 66

Paint pigments 66
Palladous chloride 60, 63
Paper chromatography 33, 85, 95
    "around a circle" 97
    one dimensional 96

Phenylhydrazine 51, 58
Phosphate
    identification of 62, 63
Plastic filters (PVC) 68
Platinum
    identification of 52, 58
Polarography 87
Potassium
    determination of 78
    identification of 55, 59
    separation of 44
Potassium chromate 49, 57
Potassium ferrocyanide 39, 42, 52,
    54, 58, 59, 72, 78
Potassium thiocyanate 52, 58
Precipitation with hydrogen sulph-
    hide 20
Purity of reagents 67
Pyrogallol 61, 63

Quinalizarine 53, 54, 59, 77, 78
Quinine 64

Radioactive substances 93
Rhodamine B 38, 42, 51, 58
Ring colorimetry 70
Ring electrography 88
Ring oven 15
Rubber 66
Rubeanic acid see Dithio-oxamide

Sample pipette 22
Selenium
    separation of 47
Silver
    identification of 49, 57
    separation of 44
Sodium
    identification of 55, 59
Sodium rhodizonate 37, 42, 49, 54,
    57, 59, 61, 63
Sodium stannite 37, 42, 50, 57
Sodiumtetraphenylboron 55, 59, 78
Spot analysis 12
Spot tests in Inorganic Analysis
    37, 48

Spot Tests in Organic Analysis, 95
Stannous chloride 49, 51, 52, 57, 58, 65
Strontium
  identification of 54, 59
  separation of 45, 47
Sulphanilic acid 61, 63
Sulphate
  identification of 61, 63
Sulphide
  identification of 61, 63
Sulphite
  identification of 61, 63

Tellurium
  separation of 47
Textiles 66
Thallium
  separation of 47
Thallous nitrate 60, 63
Thiocyanate
  identification of 60, 63
Thorium
  separation of 47
Tin
  identification of 38, 42, 51, 58
  separation of 34, 36, 47
Titanium
  identification of 41, 42, 53, 59

Titanium
  separation of 34, 36, 47
o-Tolidine 50, 57
Trace analysis 66
Transfer into a second filter 27
Tungsten
  identification of 51, 58
  separation of 47, 64
Turmeric 62, 63

Universal standard scale 80
Uranium
  determination of 78
  identification of 54, 59
  separation of 47, 65
Vanadium
  identification of 51, 58
  separation of 47

Weighted average 76

Zinc
  determination of 78, 83
  identification of 40, 42, 53, 59
  separation of 34, 36, 45, 47
Zirconium
  identification of 54, 59
  separation of 44, 47